DEFECTIVE MEDICINE

*Risk, Anger, and
the Malpractice Crisis*

Louise Lander

FARRAR, STRAUS AND GIROUX

NEW YORK

FIRST EDITION, 1978

Acknowledgment is made to the publishers and authors for
permission to quote from the following: *The Management
of the Doctor-Patient Relationship* by Richard H. Blum,
copyright © 1960 by Richard H. Blum, McGraw-Hill Book
Company; "Caring for the Patient—A Thrice-Told Tale" by
Alex M. Burgess and Alex M. Burgess, Jr., *New England
Journal of Medicine* (Vol. 274, 1966); *Life in the Ward* by
Rose Laub Coser, copyright © 1962 by Rose Laub Coser,
Michigan State University Press; *Doctoring Together:
A Study of Professional Social Control* by Eliot Freidson,
copyright © 1976 by Eliot Freidson, Elsevier Scientific Pub-
lishing Company; *Such Good Friends* by Lois Gould, copy-
right © 1970 by Lois Gould, Random House; *Psychological
Stress: Psychoanalytic and Behavioral Studies of Surgical
Patients* by Irving L. Janis, copyright © 1958 by Irving L.
Janis, John Wiley and Sons

Dimord.
6.40
8-78

To Arline Caldwell, M.D.

Contents

INTRODUCTION   ix

I. RISK AND ANGER

1 From Unhappy Patient to Angry Litigant   3

2 The Setting of Modern Medical Practice   16

3 The Tools of Modern Medical Practice   34

4 The Agents of Modern Medical Practice   57

5 The Financing of Modern Medical Practice   68

6 The Ideology of Modern Medical Practice   78

7 The Commodification of Healing   92

II. THE MALPRACTICE CRISIS

8 The Malpractice Crisis as Distortion   103

9 The Malpractice Debate as Distortion   121

10 The Malpractice Crisis as Vicious Circle   131

11 The Futility of Official Responses   143

12 The Dilemmas of Reform   169

NOTES   191

INDEX   237

Introduction

THIS is a book about appearance and reality. It aspires to be a guidebook through two territories that many people find alien and confusing—the medical malpractice debate and the structure of medical practice. It intends, in fact, to show that alienation and confusion are natural reactions when questions of life and death, anxiety and pain are converted into questions of superspecialized technology and medical economics.

The appearance we are concerned with presents the medical malpractice problem as something wrong with the insurance industry, the legal system, and/or perhaps 5 percent of physicians. The reality is that the defects of the insurance and legal systems and the incompetence of individual practitioners, however real, have been used to mask the fundamental defect of a system of medical practice that increasingly creates new risks of injury while it simultaneously denies the humanity of those people who become its patients. Rising numbers of malpractice claims—which reflect both a medical mishap and a patient angry enough to do something aggressively hostile about it—are a natural result.

The disjunction between appearance and reality is the reason this book purports to be about medical malpractice but spends relatively little space dealing with insurance economics, legal doctrines, or dispute-resolving mechanisms. To the extent these are considered, they are relegated to Part II, so that we can first explore the evolving dynamics of modern medical practice in terms of what about it makes frustration and resentment an almost inevitable concomitant of patienthood. Part I thus takes what most people already know about the structure of medical practice—that it is increasingly institutionalized, technologized, superspecialized, bureaucratized, and expensive—and looks at these more-or-less familiar trends with a new perception. That perception follows the common-sense insight that a malpractice claim has two essential aspects—the objective aspect of a medical injury and the subjective aspect of an angry patient. Looking at the various characteristics that have come to define modern medical practice, we can see in each an increase in both the objective risk of injury and the subjective effect of creating alienation, anxiety, frustration, and, potentially, anger in the increasingly dehumanized patient. The end result is the patient reduced to defective commodity, the doctor reduced to superskilled, overpaid technologist, and the doctor-patient relationship reduced to negotiating table at best, battleground at worst. An increase in malpractice claims becomes only the most obvious symptom of the inevitable increase in patient dissatisfaction.

From this point of view, we can see the immediacies of the malpractice crisis, spelled out in Part II, as reflections of the power of vested interests to shape and distort the public perception of a social problem and in that way avoid coming to grips with its fundamental reality. The final chapter then examines three manifestations of patient discontent—medical consumerism, medical self-care, and medical self-help—that attempt to go beyond the single-shot, after-the-fact response of a malpractice claim. Each, we discover, can offer ways to ameliorate particular aspects of the problem in particular situations, but none breaks free of the stultifying ideology that mystifies medical practice and refuses to acknowledge the human reality of sickness.

In sum, this is not a how-to book or even a this-is-what-you-should-lobby-for book. Rather, it is a book that seeks to begin the sometimes painful but ultimately liberating process of unmasking the underlying dynamics of a serious social problem: the almost universal dissatisfaction of its recipients with modern American medical practice, of which the malpractice phenomenon is but the most conspicuous sign.

Regrettably, there is no way to engage in such an analytical process without providing material that can then be used in a gross distortion of one's original purpose. It is possible, for example, although certainly not intended, that parts of this book could be used as a primer on how doctors and hospital personnel can engage in psychological manipulation of patients to ward off malpractice suits; a hospital administrator, for example, might cite portions of what follows to buttress his argument to a doubting board of trustees that hiring someone called a patient representative would be a worthwhile investment in litigation prevention. It should go without saying that this does not mean the book is an endorsement of any approach that merely papers over structural defects, with whatever success in the short run.

On the other hand, the book does lend itself to various legitimate uses. Readers who would welcome a systematic exploration of what it is about modern medical practice that generates chronic dissatisfaction but who are less than eager to delve into the technical issues surrounding malpractice (at least while the subject is off the front pages) could limit themselves to Part I and the final chapter. Those who seek to understand the technicalities of the immediate malpractice crisis without exploring fully the evolving structure of modern medicine could make do with the first chapter and Part II. Both approaches, of course, give up a lot, but at least they do not distort.

Language being a sometimes treacherous medium of expression, it is necessary to provide an explanation for two characteristics of the language of what follows. First, those who commonly read books in this general field may find this one sounding strange, even archaic, because it quite deliberately avoids using the terms "health care" and "the health-care-delivery system," speaking instead of "medical treatment" and "the structure of medical practice." Although some have argued that the widespread shift in the 1970's to the term "health" as a substitute for "medical" "challenges the health professional to achieve higher standards of care on a broader, interdisciplinary level," [1] the more likely effect is the propagation of a myth—that people who interact with the so-called health-care-delivery system are treated in more than narrowly medical terms. "But if thought corrupts language, language can also corrupt thought," as Orwell expressed the problem.[2] To speak of "health care" would corrupt thought in the sense of making it difficult to see that what is wrong with what goes on in the name of making sick people well is precisely that it is not care and that it has nothing to do with health. (Physicians may argue that the word "medical" cannot properly be used in connection with the work of, say, nurses, because only a physician is legally entitled to perform medical acts—one of the few instances in which doctors think like lawyers—but they should be willing to acknowledge that the work of so-called health workers in all cases conforms to the assumptions of the medical model.)

Second, I must admit to having met defeat in my attempt to write a book that does not to some extent ratify the sexism of the English language, in particular its designation of a generic human being as "he." While in many cases the obvious devices of using plural forms, repeating the generic noun, or recasting the entire sentence have provided a means of evading the problem, one unbudgeable stumbling block has remained. This stems from the need I have felt to consider a prototypical patient and a prototypical doctor, abstracted from the unique characteristics of individual patients and individual doctors. In many cases it simply will not do to write "patients . . . they" or "doctors . . . they"; the only way to express the intended point is in terms of "the patient . . . he" or "the doctor . . . he." (To write "the patient . . . she" and "the doctor . . . he" would conform to the statistically most common situation but would only perpetuate other sexist preconceptions.) To write "the patient . . . he or she" and "the doctor . . . he or she" might conquer sexism but in the process would destroy the sense of a unitary prototype independent of gender.

L.L.

I

Risk and Anger

I

From Unhappy Patient to Angry Litigant

*I see a malpractice suit as a sort of reverse class action suit—
one individual suing the entire medical profession as a way
of getting even for all the psychic insults of long delays in
crowded waiting rooms and doctors with too little time to give
each patient.* ELI BERNZWEIG, former Executive Director,
HEW Secretary's Commission on Medical Malpractice

*To write prescriptions is easy, but to come to an understand-
ing with people is hard.* FRANZ KAFKA, "A Country Doctor"

THE medical press was triumphant; on June 1, 1976,
after over a year of nothing but disaster to report on
the malpractice front, a victory had finally been scored on
the side of the medical profession. A doctor sued for malpractice had had the guts to sue his patient back, and a
jury in Chicago had found the patient, her husband, and
her lawyers liable for "willful and wanton involvement in
litigation without reasonable cause" and the lawyers also
liable for legal malpractice.

One of the exuberant articles recording that landmark
event was written by the doctor-plaintiff himself, a radiologist named Dr. Leonard Berlin, who took to the pages
of *Medical Economics* (the *Cosmopolitan* of the medical
profession) to tell his story to his fellow physicians.[1] That
story does vindicate Dr. Berlin in the sense of making his
medical and legal innocence convincing. But, more to the
point, his story inadvertently reveals what motivates patients
to take the extraordinary step of hauling their doctors into
court.

[3]

Mrs. Harriet Nathan injured the little finger of her right hand playing tennis and went to the emergency room of a suburban Chicago hospital, where Dr. Berlin had an office in the radiology department. He supervised the taking of a series of X rays, made a diagnosis, and sent her on to see an orthopedic surgeon named Dr. William Meltzer. Dr. Meltzer's treatment, which apparently followed generally accepted orthopedic procedures, nonetheless failed to completely relieve the pain and deformity of the injured finger.

Five months after the injury, Dr. Berlin relates in his article, he was telephoned by Mrs. Nathan's husband, Gilbert, who told him that "his wife's finger was deformed and still painful, and that they were both angry at Dr. Meltzer. The orthopedist, Gilbert said, had not taken Harriet's injury seriously, and had been rude and abrupt. Gilbert intimated that they might bring a malpractice suit against Meltzer, and that if they did, they'd 'have to involve' me, too."

What Mr. Nathan said over the telephone reflects precisely those elements of a doctor-patient encounter that are indispensable to a patient's decision to bring a malpractice suit. Actual medical malpractice—professional performance that demonstrably falls below professional standards—is not indispensable. Some sort of injury or unhappy outcome *is* indispensable; here no one disputed that Mrs. Nathan's hand was permanently deformed, and we may assume that it gave her pain and made certain activities difficult or impossible. But the injury, the objective sign that something went wrong, is not sufficient; injury by itself does not translate into the intense hostility that a lawsuit expresses. That objective sign must be joined with the subjective state of being angry—here the Nathans' natural reaction to their perception that Dr. Meltzer "had not taken Harriet's injury seriously, and had been rude and abrupt." The anger is usually provoked by a doctor, although increasingly hospitals are finding themselves defending lawsuits that reflect anger at their employees. And the rules of the legal game may result in the targets of the legal maneuvers being different from, or broader than, the original object of the patient's anger, as Dr. Berlin discovered when he was drawn into the net cast by the Nathans' anger at his colleague.

We should therefore grant at the outset what many doctors, for their own purposes, loudly insist on: that there is a difference between actual malpractice and a malpractice suit or claim. But we should dwell for a moment, as those doctors would prefer not to, on the fact that a patient who becomes a malpractice claimant has suffered an injury—even if it is euphemistically called "an untoward result of treatment." And we should note that the injured patient, as he attempts to cope with pain, disappointment, and economic loss, rarely has the means of knowing at the outset whether negligence, fluke, or some unalterable body process is responsible for his misery.

Conversely—to complete the picture—we should note that there can be malpractice in the sense of medical negligence without its causing injury. A doctor, for example, may stupidly make an erroneous diagnosis, but the treatment he prescribes for what he mistakenly thinks is wrong may turn out to be substantially the same as the treatment of choice for what is really wrong. Or the doctor may fail to discover, for example, that the patient has terminal cancer, but escape blame because by the time the patient consulted him, it was too late to do anything anyway. The universe of medical injuries and the universe of medical negligence overlap, then, but do not coincide, and while malpractice as a legal concept declares both injury and negligence to be equally indispensable, malpractice claims as a social eruption declare the supremacy of injury.

Data on the size of either the universe of medical injuries or the universe of medical negligence are so scattered and fragmentary as to be essentially useless.[2] There are, however, a few statistical indications that the universe of injuries is enormously larger than the universe of malpractice claims, a disproportion that confirms the notion that although a medical injury is necessary to a malpractice claim, it is not by itself sufficient to trigger one. A federally sponsored interview study conducted in 1972, for example, found that over 40 percent of the sample had had some "negative medical care experience"; of those, over 85 percent believed that some kind of medical failure had been involved, but only 8 percent had even considered seeking legal advice. Even of those who had suffered major permanent injury from what they perceived as a medical failure, only about 35 percent had considered consulting a lawyer.[3] A Louis Harris poll conducted in 1975 reported that 15 percent of those interviewed thought that they or someone close to them had been the victim of malpractice, but that only 6 percent of those had tried to bring suit.[4]

Another statistical tidbit implies not only that the number of injuries overwhelms the number of claims but that what a medical or hospital observer perceives as an injury differs from what a patient perceives as an injury, and one worth filing a claim about. A risk-management program of an unnamed hospital association generated about 700,000 reports of unusual incidents (such as equipment failures, anesthesia deaths, slips and falls) over a twenty-year period. During the same period only 15,000 malpractice claims were filed, and 85 percent of these involved incidents that were *not* reported.[5]

What distinguishes the injuries that do not become malpractice claims from the injuries that do, and what even colors the patient's perception of what constitutes an injury, is the subjective element of patient anger; without anger, an act as hostile as a lawsuit, particularly against as well-established an authority figure as a physician, is impossible to contemplate. Thus, while for legal purposes medical malpractice represents the intersection of patient injury and physician negligence, for social purposes a malpractice claim represents the intersection of patient injury and patient anger.

Assorted categories of authoritative observers, as they have attempted to explain to physicians what the malpractice explosion is all about and how they can avoid being burned by it, have explicitly or implicitly recognized that patient anger is critically important. A psychiatrist writing in a medical journal advises his colleagues in organic medicine that "attorney friends . . . tell me of a triad of client complaints which may lead to litigation. First is an adverse result of treatment; second is the feeling in the mind of the patient and of sympathetic listeners who may some day constitute a jury that 'this shouldn't have happened.' Add to this a patient who feels disappointed, hurt and angry towards the doctor." [6]

A psychologist dispensing advice to doctors in a book on problems of "management" of the doctor-patient relationship puts it more bluntly:

> The doctor who *wants* to get in trouble after an incident of actual malpractice can do so easily. All he has to do is to avoid the patient, blame the patient for the bad result, refuse to talk to the family, refuse to apologize, refuse to listen in humility to patient castigation, and then to send his bill as usual. The doctor who wants to guarantee a breakdown in the relationship does not have to do *all* of the foregoing, just a few will suffice. The doctor who does not want to be sued will avoid these traps and will face the patient with humble sympathy and courage for the truth. [7]

A logical counterpart to that diatribe is an observation by the then executive director of a federal commission investigating the malpractice problem: "In this whole field of malpractice litigation there is a strong get-even, or revenge, factor. I have heard plaintiffs' attorneys say that their clients did not really want to sue for money. What they really wanted was a chance to be alone in the room with the defendant doctor for about fifteen minutes." [8]

And there is a particular breed of physician who provokes the desire for revenge. In the words of an attorney who specializes in defending doctors in malpractice suits: "The typical physician who gets sued for malpractice is the surgeon who will read *The Wall Street Journal* while the jury is out. He's got the businessman's personality, and it shows in the way he runs his practice. He's usually the one who has eight patients in six rooms, with half a dozen more in the waiting room, and with a flock of nurses checking Blue Shield cards. He's also arrogant, egotistical, condescending, aloof." At the same time, "there probably isn't a person I know who hasn't at some time received subpar medical care. Yet they do not go around suing doctors. That's because they think of their doctors as human beings." [9]

Despite the offensiveness of the notion of doctors engaging in psychological manipulation of patients for the sake of self-protection, the literature of expert advice on how to avoid malpractice claims is instructive for what it tells us about the importance to those claims of the subjective element in the doctor-patient situation. A malpractice insurance carrier, for example, advises its doctor-customers: "Warm up to your patients—if you show a genuine interest in their problems, they're far more likely to forgive and forget when there's a bad medical result." [10] Another carrier's newsletter cautions doctors against subjecting their patients to long waits: "A wait of more than fifteen minutes at the most means to patients not that the doctor is a little behind or a little disorganized, but that he does not care." [11]

It is generally agreed that money can become a catalyst of intense patient anger. "It's well known," according to one legal authority, "that aggressive collection activities

have triggered many malpractice suits." [12] "It's risky to dun
a patient to pay his bill," warns another lawyer in a medical magazine. "A rather minimal unpaid fee can sometimes
turn into an expensive lawsuit." [13] A third lawyer writes of
an interview with a patient determined to sue a doctor
who'd failed to diagnose a broken bone: "The patient's
anger was far out of proportion to his pain and incon-
venience, so I kept probing until we came to the part of the
story that brought everything into focus. 'That incompetent
so-and-so had the gall to send me a bill for $17.50, and
when I called up to complain about it, he wouldn't even
come to the phone,' the man shouted." [14]

A psychologist advises doctors:

> Billing procedures in every case of a poor result should be
> individualized. Contrary to the rationale of some insurance
> carriers that any modification in billing may be interpreted
> as an admission of guilt, the author would suggest that suits
> are much more likely to be filed just because the bill comes
> "as usual" and the doctor acted "just like nothing had gone
> wrong." The bill will be interpreted as a symptom of the
> doctor's "not giving a damn," and like so many other
> money matters, it becomes the focus for intense feeling. [15]

Perhaps the connection between money and anger is the
implicit message that the bill conveys to the patient (who
by hypothesis is already unhappy with the result of treatment): "The doctor sees me only as a source of income—
a money-machine—not as a human being." And perhaps
recognition as a (sick or injured) human being is a more
important expectation to the patient than his expectation
that the doctor will make him well again; thus, the lack of
such recognition, as implied by the bill-as-usual, is much
more angering than the fact of not being quite well again.

Not all angry, injured patients, it must be acknowledged,
sue their doctors. Doctor-suing represents the extreme end
of a spectrum of angry conduct that includes not paying the
doctor's bill, [16] changing doctors, [17] going to healers not

sanctioned by organized medicine,[18] and, paradoxically perhaps, not complying with the doctor's instructions.[19]

Nor does the increase in malpractice suits reflect merely an increase in the number of angry, injured patients. It has had to reflect as well a legal system (including lawyers to litigate the cases) that is more and more receptive to suits by patients against their doctors. But it is the medical system, not the legal system, that initiates the process that transforms an unhappy patient into an angry litigant; and if increasing malpractice suits are not a symptom of increasing malpractice, they are nonetheless a symptom, an external sign of internal dysfunction—in this case dysfunction in the bases of medical practice.

The injury and the anger that combine in a malpractice claim can each be linked to a counterpart in medical practice, an element that transcends the individual psychologies of particular patients and particular doctors. The counterpart of injury is risk; the counterpart of anger is what one might call an anger-inducing situation. And what the leaders of American scientific medicine call the miracles of medical progress are frequently procedures, settings, and mind-sets that, whatever else they are, are increasingly risky and increasingly angering.

"The average doctor has been transformed in sixty years [since 1910] from an incompetent physician, whose strength lay in the 'bedside manner' of his mystique, to a specialist internist, surgeon, or endocrinologist whose own competence is buttressed by an array of diagnostic and treatment aids and techniques. American doctors are among the best trained, perhaps *the* best-trained technological physicians in the world." [20] This description, by a liberal scholar whose primary concern was that this technological expertise be made equally available to all, implicitly expresses both the source of the growing risk of injury and the source of the growing numbers of patients left feeling cheated and therefore angry.

That "array of diagnostic and treatment aids and techniques" is itself an ever-expanding source of risk. As scientific medicine develops ever more sophisticated and ever more invasive techniques of diagnosis and treatment, it thereby multiplies the possibility of serious physical harm to the patient through mistake, accident, or malfunction. The bureaucratic, superspecialized setting in which these techniques are increasingly carried out—the modern hospital—embodies its own set of risks in its multiple sources of decision-making, its frequently garbled communications, and its sheer bigness.

A more subtle source of risk, and ultimately of anger, is the change in the role of the physician described by the scholar quoted above. The "incompetent physician" was, in his unscientific way, a comforter and healer of the sick person, although his most potent treatment may have been the placebo effect. His modern American successor is less a healer than a highly trained, highly compensated technocrat, and he applies his technological knowledge and skill less to the sick person than to an objectified set of symptoms. But that objectified set of symptoms is only a part of the patient's sickness, and its treatment calls on only a part of the healing process inherent in the patient. And that bureaucratic, superspecialized setting in which objectified sets of symptoms are most scientifically dealt with dilutes and distorts whatever healing effect the modern American physician might inadvertently generate in one-to-one contact with his patient. The patient's anatomy is thoroughly probed, his bodily processes thoroughly monitored, and his bodily fluids thoroughly tested; he's thoroughly drugged and/or his organs are thoroughly rearranged; his health insurer and/or his bank account are thoroughly tapped for payment; but something important is frequently left untouched (or maybe gets mangled), and as a result his sickness may not be thoroughly cared for.

It is commonly said, even by physicians, that medical

care has become increasingly impersonal. That comment is in a sense true, but it is so incomplete as to be a distortion. For it implicitly lumps medical care together with all the transactions of modern life, as though the consequences of a depersonalized doctor-patient relationship were comparable to the consequences of a depersonalized grocer-customer relationship. The critical difference of course reflects the meaning and effect of being sick, "a grossly uncomfortable, often painful, often embarrassing, frequently terrorizing experience involving the fundamental character of the self." [21] And, independent of how helpless we may actually feel when we are sick, we are taught from childhood that, with the exception of trivial symptoms, sickness is a crisis that we can surmount only by calling on the unique skills of the doctor.[22]

So that he may exercise those peculiar skills freely, we then grant the doctor extraordinary privileges. The doctor's physical examination "is probably the only occasion in ordinary life when an adult renders to another so much of his freedom, dignity, and responsibility. It is one of the few occasions when the adult voluntarily exposes himself to pain and embarrassment with an implicit agreement not to retreat or defend." [23] Submitting to treatment may, then, require extraordinary sacrifice: "The burdens the physician asks his patients and their families to assume on his advice are often very severe. They include suffering—you 'have to get worse before you can get better,' as for instance in the case of a major surgical operation. They include risk of death, permanent or lengthy disablement, severe financial costs and various others." [24]

Our willingness to grant the doctor such privileges and to undertake such burdens because he wants us to requires that we trust him to alleviate our misery in the process. "The patient's relationship with the physician is based on the patient's surrender of his pathology to the physician. The patient will not surrender his pathology unless he believes that he is surrendering it to a competent and trust-worthy person." [25] That trust can itself be a source of heal-ing power: "It is well known that patients often feel better the moment the doctor comes into the house. Your [the doctor's] presence, especially if you have helped in the past, produces this effect because it promises relief of pain (or other symptoms of the pathological process) and the allay-ing of anxiety." [26]

The effectiveness of the patient's trust in the doctor, how-ever, has much to do with the doctor's attitude toward the patient. This effect is reflected, for example, in the results of studies of the placebo effect:

> The interested doctor who imparts confidence, who is friendly and reassuring to patients, who performs a thor-ough examination, and who is not anxious, conflicted, or guilty about the patient or his treatment is more likely to elicit positive placebo reactions. Negative placebo reac-tions are more likely when the doctor is angry, rejecting, and contemptuous toward patients or seriously preoccupied with his own problems. Cures may occur when the patient perceives the physician's strong need for the patient to im-prove, and does so in order to gratify the doctor.[27]

Modern scientific medicine, however, has little stomach for such stuff. Insofar as it recognizes the non-rational at all, it relegates that sphere to a separate scientific discipline, namely, psychiatry (the more enlightened physicians ac-knowledging that psychiatry is a scientific discipline). That evasive tactic frees the orthopedist, for example, from recognizing any obligation to deal with the anxieties of the patient with the fractured hip, who is probably more traumatized by the fact of his now-limited mobility than by the physical injury itself.

Conflict then arises from the disparity between the pa-tient's expectations of the role the doctor will undertake—expectations that are the basis of the trust he places in the doctor—and the doctor's own view of his role. The patient, that is, is probably seeking a healer and comforter, while the doctor, proud of his specialized technological expertise, consciously or unconsciously scorns such a role as anachronistic, unscientific, and too time-consuming for his busy schedule. To the patient, his anxieties about his future, however irrational, are part of his sickness; to the doctor, only physical, preferably observable, pathology is worthy of his attention. It's as if a person set out to hire a chamber orchestra and all he could get was Muzak.

Thus, the anger-inducing situation in medical practice that may trigger the anger expressed in a malpractice claim is one in which the patient feels that he was cheated and his trust was betrayed, probably because he found his humanity being reduced to discrete, isolated pathology. To quote the psychologist advising doctors again: "The doctor who thinks of the patient only as a specimen of a disease, 'that kidney in room 41,' . . . is likely to produce an upset patient. The patient becomes upset because he feels that the doctor has deprived him of dignity. The patient senses that his relationship with the doctor is not a relationship of one person to another, but of a person (the doctor) to a thing (the disease)." [28] Mrs. Nathan and her husband were angry at her orthopedist because he "had not taken Harriet's injury seriously," because, in other words, he had failed to recognize the human trauma of a permanently deformed right hand.

If the doctor fails to fulfill the patient's expectations of his role—if he treats the patient's sickness not as a human condition but as an isolated entity—then the patient in his anger feels free to violate the proscriptions of the patient role. If being passive and submissive, as a "good patient" is expected to be, has brought a person grief, then he may look for a way to right this wrong that is active and aggressive; bringing a lawsuit, whatever its drawbacks, is at least that.

In short, the dysfunction of which the malpractice problem is a symptom is modern American medical practice itself, which has transformed healers into technocrats, sick people into objectified symptoms, sickness into disease entities, and the healing relationship into a depersonalized economic transaction. The fact of that transformation takes many distinct forms and reflects the interwoven effects of many distinct social, economic, and ideological forces. What follows is an attempt both to delineate the pieces of the puzzle and to set out the totality of how they fit together.

2

The Setting of Modern
Medical Practice

Concern for the Patient *is as important a prerequisite for membership on the Mount Herman [Hospital] staff as allegiance to* The American Way of Life *is for citizenship. The Patient, with a capital "P," may be an effective symbol, like the common man, the worker, the whole child. But the individual patient tends to remain, in practice, an object or a "case." He is then seen not as the living human being who struggles, in his physical powerlessness, with the problem of his identity and autonomy; but as something to be "managed," like a thing.* ROSE LAUB COSER, *Life in the Ward*

People tell you that they're not afraid of hospitals but they don't like doctors. The first is not true. They are very very afraid. The second is true. They don't like doctors but what they really fear is illness.
A hospitalized patient, quoted in *Sickness and Society* by Raymond S. Duff and August B. Hollingshead

THE hospital—or, more fashionably, the "medical center"—has almost replaced the stethoscope as the symbol of medical treatment. From its medieval infancy as refuge for weary travelers and its eighteenth-century adolescence as welfare institution and death house, the hospital has emerged into adulthood as the matrix in which modern medical practice plies its proudest achievements. As such, the hospital and the situation of the hospitalized patient have an intimate connection with the malpractice equation of injury and anger. In much condensed form, this connective chain links the increased likelihood that a sick person will find himself in a hospital, the inherently frightening and potentially angering character of the experience of being a hospital patient, the physical and organizational risks inherent in the hospital as a physical and social institution, and the hospital's function as the setting for the most risky maneuvers of modern scientific medicine.

Over the last twenty-five years or so, one's chances of finding oneself in the hospital have risen by half. In more precise statistical terms, the annual rate of admissions to short-term hospitals (other than psychiatric and tuberculosis hospitals) has gone from 110 per 1,000 population in 1950 to 165 in 1974, a rise of 50 percent.[1] (The rise in the number of short-term hospital beds per 1,000 population—from 3.3 to 4.4—was about 33 percent in the same period,[2] the lesser figure probably reflecting the fact that hospitals have tended to operate with an increasing proportion of their beds filled and to keep their patients for decreasing numbers of days per illness.) The size of the hospital in which one finds oneself has been growing at a similar rate—from an average of 100 beds for short-term hospitals in 1950 to an average of 156 beds in 1974.[3] Oddly enough, the leading diagnostic classification of hospitalized patients in 1972 was something called "signs, symptoms, and ill-defined conditions." [4]

In 1954, doctor-patient encounters in hospitals accounted for about 10 percent of all doctor-patient encounters; by 1970, that proportion had more than doubled, to 21 percent.[5] To that juxtaposition, which reflects the progressive displacement of the home and the doctor's office by the hospital as the site of medical treatment, it is instructive to add that those roughly 20 percent of doctor-patient encounters produce roughly 80 percent of malpractice claims. About 80 percent of the incidents that become the basis of a malpractice claim, in other words, take place somewhere in a hospital.[6]

The increasing concentration of medical practice in the hospital reflects the confluence of a number of economic,

social, and technological considerations. The beds have
been there; since shortly after World War II the federal
government (through the Hill-Burton Act of 1946) has in
effect been the guarantor of an adequate supply of hospital
beds, subsidizing the construction of about 365,000 of them
in almost four thousand communities between 1947 and
1974.[7] The means to pay the bill has been there; since
health insurance became a subject of collective bargaining
in the 1940's, the doctor has increasingly been able to assume that financial considerations need not stand in the
way of his desire to hospitalize a patient. (Whereas only
about 9 percent of the population had private hospital insurance in 1940, that proportion became 51 percent in
1950, 75 percent in 1962, and 87 percent in 1973.[8])

As it has become easier to put the patient in the hospital,
it has simultaneously become harder to care for him at
home. The disappearance of household help, maiden aunts,
and grandmothers from the American family unit has
meant that hospitalization of a seriously ill member serves
the social function of sparing the nuclear household, with
its limited caring resources, from a possibly intolerable
strain.[9]

Of course, the preferred rationale among doctors for their
growing use of the hospital as the setting of medical practice is the technological one. In the words of one eminent
academic physician: "In the past half-century scientific and
technological developments have contributed so heavily to
the diagnosis, treatment and prevention of disease that it is
no longer possible for the physician to work effectively
without the modern apparatus and the specialists and technicians centralized in the hospital." [10]

While it is obviously true that surgery in the home no
longer makes technological sense and that putting a cobalt
bomb in a doctor's office would be grossly uneconomic,
there are considerations of cost-effectiveness, convenience,
and control that from the physician's point of view are

equally compelling in making the decision to hospitalize.
With patients who need both to stay flat on their backs and
to be checked on daily, centralizing their location in the
hospital (a trend that began when house calls were not yet
historical relics) effects a significant savings in the doctor's
time,[11] a commodity that has become increasingly valuable
in the literal sense. Hospitalization also provides a logistically simple means for the physician (especially a gener-
alist) to arrange a consultation—with an intern, resident,
or another attending physician—while maintaining his identity as "my doctor" in the patient's eyes.[12] Or the presence
of house staff in a teaching hospital simply permits the admitting physician to concentrate his energies on those of his
patients who remain in the outside world, reasoning that the
constant readiness that is the ostensible state of the modern
medical center diminishes his responsibility for those he has
consigned to its care.[13] (By 1960 almost half of all hospital
beds were in hospitals that offered internships and residencies.[14])

The doctor saves on his office overhead costs for equipment and personnel when he uses the hospital setting to
perform a procedure that is simple and safe enough to be
carried out in a doctor's office.[15] For the purpose of controlling the environment of his patient—what he does and
what is done to him—the doctor finds the hospital and its
staff more reliable than the patient's home and family.[16]
And whether or not the hospital's modern diagnostic laboratory and its impressive array of equipment and facilities
were the main motivation for hospitalizing the patient to
begin with, once he's settled down in their midst it will seem
only logical to take advantage of their capabilities.

From the perspective of the patient, what is logistically
convenient and technologically superior about the hospital
is buried in an avalanche of what is remote, impersonal,
rigid, and alien. Just when the miseries and anxieties of
serious illness make a person need most the comfort and

reassurance that familiar surroundings can provide, he is abruptly deposited, like Alice falling down the rabbit hole, into an entirely foreign place, peopled by a citizenry who rush about in strange (but uncolorful) costumes, muttering a language that is only sometimes familiar, whose primary interest is in such irrelevant attributes as his Blue Cross number and his childhood illnesses, and who make it perfectly clear that he is expected to conform to their apparently arbitrary customs without benefit of any explanation. Unlike other foreign countries the visitor may have been to, this one constrains him from picking up and leaving, and on the instructions of someone he may have thought of as an ally, if not a friend, but who turns out instead to be one of the foreigners—his doctor.[17]

The patient's loss of his familiar surroundings is rapidly followed by the loss of most of those personal belongings that symbolize his identity—clothes, jewelry, the odds and ends in pockets or purse. In exchange he acquires what seems to symbolize both his risk of being misidentified and his status as an objective piece of pathology—a plastic identification bracelet.

Having been extracted from his day-to-day world and stripped of his day-to-day belongings, the patient has still more to lose. His privacy and his ability to exert some control over what he does and what is done to him have been sacrificed to the task-oriented functioning of his institutional host. His room is constantly invaded by total strangers who, usually without introduction or explanation, poke and probe, insert assorted substances into his body via assorted routes and extract assorted other substances via assorted other routes, and determine his waking and eating habits and most other details of a life that is no longer his own. His senses are subjected to abrasive noises, harsh light, and unpleasant odors, all of which he is powerless to banish.

The patient's powerlessness is exacerbated by the strangeness of his environment and what goes on in it, a state that its functionaries do little to alleviate. On the contrary, even the familiar may be made foreign, as when the nurse asks the patient whether he has voided, as if to urinate (much less pee) would be insufficiently clinical.

Trapped in this discomforting situation, not of his making and which he is incapable of changing, the patient may look to his doctor, who put him there, for reassurance and hope. But his doctor most likely sees hospital rounds as involving the minimum monitoring necessary for clinical and fee-charging purposes. One hospital study that timed patient encounters with their doctors found that the mean time spent by doctors in the patient's room was about four-tenths of a minute in private rooms and two-tenths of a minute in semiprivate rooms.[18] Another study found that the patient's greatest problem with his doctor's visits was their being so short that asking questions was impossible—" 'They don't stand still long enough for you to draw a bead on um,' " as one patient put it.[19]

The doctor's rush is but one aspect of the fact that the relative position of doctor vis-à-vis patient undergoes a dramatic change when the hospital replaces the home as the site of medical care. "In a private home the physician is an intruder, coming hat in hand, apologetic because he has worn his rubbers inside the hallway, and feeling that he is disturbing the routines of the household." [20] In the hospital, however, not only is the doctor not the intruder, but his superiority over the patient is made evident by everything that happens. "For example, if patient and doctor both speak to the nurse at once, the nurse will answer the doctor, not the patient. If an orderly enters the room where the doctor and patient are present, the orderly greets the doctor first. He may not greet the patient at all." [21] Rather than alleviating the patient's sense of aloneness and inferiority, the doctor-patient encounter is likely to reinforce it.

(When a physician has the misfortune to be hospitalized, he expresses amazement at what from the other end of the stethoscope he observes, but does not really see, every working day. To quote one article by a physician turned hospital patient: "It was an odd sensation; a man seems to lose his dignity when he puts on one of those [hospital] gowns. . . . I would spend ten minutes or so turning about, trying to find a comfortable position. Just as I succeeded, a technician would enter my room to take some blood. . . . Fear of the unknown, of what is happening, can be the worst experience a patient goes through in a hospital." [22])

Sometimes the ultimate strangeness of the hospital is the contradictoriness of its expectations as the patient's stay progresses. Having been bombarded with signals that he is to relinquish his worldly responsibilities and become dependent and passive, the patient whose discharge has been ordered, frequently on very short notice, is suddenly expected to do an emotional about-face and, like Cinderella at midnight, undergo a complete and instantaneous transformation, in this case back to a state of worldly independence.[23]

One might think that all these dehumanizing (not to say inhumane) characteristics of the hospital environment were but by-products of an organizational structure and mode of operation designed to maximize at least the technical efficiency of the delivery of modern medical treatment. One would, however, be wrong. There is, for example, the anomaly—a reflection of the power and independence of the American medical profession—that those with the authority to direct patient care, namely, doctors, do not maintain a continuous presence in the hospital, whereas those who do maintain such a presence, notably nurses and administrators, lack that authority. (In teaching hospitals that paradox is somewhat alleviated by the presence of interns and residents, but at the same time is further complicated by their inexperience and their focus on the hospital as a training experience.) [24]

That anomaly is but a reflection of the larger anomaly that the structure of the prototypical American hospital embodies two lines of authority: the administrative staff, which supervises its ongoing function as an institution, and the medical staff, mostly comprising independent private practitioners, who maintain final authority over patient care. And while the hospital's executive director and his underlings may be preoccupied with issues of organizational maintenance, physical and economic, that are only indirectly related to the care of patients, its physicians may well be preoccupied with the logistics and corresponding economics of their private practices, of which their hospitalized patients are only one segment. "Many of the tensions between administrators and clinicians in the American hospital are due to the fact that the American doctor is often hurried, peremptory, unaware of the results of his orders, and difficult to find. The administrator and nurse in the American hospital have the added irritant of knowing that many of the doctor's demands are designed to assist his lucrative private practice, rather than to assist the hospital." [25] Not only are there two separate lines of authority, with all the potential for confusion and conflict that implies, but neither is focused on providing optimal care, whether defined in technical or humanistic terms, for particular hospitalized patients.

Both administrative and medical lines of authority converge on the nurses, who typically insist that it is they who *really* care for the patients, in whose presence they spend their working days. But while the nursing staff as a collectivity is with patients constantly, individual nurse-patient contacts are fragmented and fleeting. Aside from the unavoidable division of a twenty-four-hour day into shifts, the work of nursing is typically further divided by task rather than by patient. Nurse Jones, that is, is not assigned to provide nursing care to Mr. Smith but, for example, to administer medication to all the patients in the nursing unit, while Nurse (or Nurse's Aide) Brown does likewise with taking vital signs or making beds, and so on.

Whatever the function served by such an arrangement—one theory sees it as a defense against the anxiety nurses might experience from sustained contact with seriously ill people [26]—it results in nurses knowing very little about the patients in their care. One study, in which several hundred nurses were interviewed about patients on their floor, found a frequent "inability to recall a particular patient or to identify him by name while the patient was still on the division or had been discharged only the day before"; perhaps more disturbingly, "less than one half of the registered nurses, about one licensed practical nurse in three, and one nurse's aide in four knew the patient's diagnosis and the treatment his physician had planned for him." The result was that "registered nurses, in the majority of instances, followed orders given by physicians and did things for patients without knowing why and how these things related to what was wrong with the person under treatment." [27]

Nursing care, in other words, is split up so as to create the necessity for close coordination within the nursing staff, while the ignorance of the patient's situation that such fragmentation creates intensifies the risk that a slip-up in coordination will have a detrimental effect on the patient. One result is a protectionist, if not successfully protective, rigidity that makes the hospital a uniquely caste-ridden subculture and leads to such sermonizing as this: "It is especially imperative in the field of health that individuals do not overreach their respective areas of competence. A glass of water given [by a nurse's aide] to a patient whose fluid intake is being restricted could conceivably be a serious interruption of therapy. Therefore careful training and jurisdictional control must be exercised at all levels." [28] That rationale is of little comfort to the patient whose fluid intake is not restricted but who can't reach his water pitcher without assistance, and it would be unnecessary if the nursing person who happened to be in the room were able to learn enough about the patient to know whether or not his fluid intake was restricted.

The most significant caste distinction in the hospital is not within nursing but between nurses and doctors, and the communication between nurses and doctors largely determines the content of patient care. Nurses, that is, primarily do to patients what is ordered by doctors and are responsible for reporting to doctors adverse events or trends in the patient's condition. Nurse-doctor communication, however, is rarely of the spoken, face-to-face variety; one sociologist observing communication on the hospital floor found that doctors were three times as likely to speak to other doctors as to a nurse and that nurses talked to other nurses seven times as frequently as they talked to doctors.[29]

Communication between doctors and nurses is usually in writing and usually travels one way only, from doctor to nurse. The doctor, that is, as part of his daily sweep through the hospital, writes in a doctor's order book his instructions for medications, diagnostic tests, special diets, or physical treatments. The justification for the written order is couched in terms of safety and accountability, but safety and accountability are undercut when the communication is only written (in possibly ambiguous and/or illegible terms), the doctor not verifying that the nurse fully understands it and the nurse not clarifying its ambiguities with the doctor, both of which could easily be accomplished in a face-to-face verbal exchange.

Similar difficulties inhere in what is supposed to be communication from nurse to doctor as to the patient's condition, effected through the medium of written nursing notes. One physician-expert on the malpractice situation has observed that "the physician seldom knows what's in the nurses' notes and is often subsequently embarrassed to find incidents recorded in the nurses' notes that failed to get into his or his staff's progress notes."[30] Nursing experts, for their part, have observed that "nurses often believe that their notes in the medical record are unimportant, that no one ever reads them, and that they are not kept as a permanent part of the record." [31] The communications system, in short, is wildly illogical in terms of efficiently transmitting critical information; its logic consists in its reflecting and reinforcing the social distance between doctors and nurses. It thus protects the status system of the hospital more than it protects the patient, whose changed condition may not come to a doctor's attention, and who in the meantime is in constant risk of being on the receiving end of a misinterpreted instruction.

What the patient will not be on the receiving end of is more than infrequent and fragmentary communication from hospital personnel. Even modern hospital architecture, intent on erasing the symbols of class distinctions among patients, has in the process conspired against their need for information. In the old open wards, patients were able to compensate in part for the lack of communication from hospital functionaries by orienting each other to hospital routine and by observing nurses and doctors working with other patients. Or patients would feel free to waylay nurses on their way through the ward with the sort of question they would find too trivial to justify ringing for an answer to in a semiprivate room.[32]

That the patient has a problem to begin with reflects the fact that the assignment system makes nurses task-oriented rather than patient-oriented, and that talking with patients more than the minimum amount necessary is not recognized as a proper assignment.[33] Nurses are, in any event, as we noted, largely ignorant of the patient's condition, and they are wary of treading on the physician's exclusive prerogative of imparting definitive information to his charges.

But the doctor, as we have seen, prefers to breeze through his patients' rooms, at less than a minute per; what few words he utters as he passes may well be in a jargon that the patient only vaguely understands and is not given a chance to ask about. " 'You wait 24 hours before you see your physician. Then he puts his head into the door, comes perhaps and takes some candy, or he talks to you in a way you don't understand and then he goes out again.' " [34]

The quick in-and-out—which could not be so easily accomplished in the patient's home or the doctor's office— is symbolic of the displacement and diffusion of responsibility that occur when the locus of medical treatment shifts to the hospital. In the patient's home or in the doctor's office, there is no one else for the doctor to pass the buck to (the workers in his office are *his* employees, unlike the workers in the hospital), whereas, in the hospital, responsibility can be shared with a variety of functionaries, not to mention the abstraction, the bureaucracy, itself.

Of the assortment of risks that a patient is subjected to in the hospital, the one perhaps most directly related to its problematic organizational structure is the risk of medication error. This is a broad classification of mishap that can mean the patient got a drug when he shouldn't have or got no drug when he should have, got the wrong drug, got the wrong dose of the right drug, or got the drug by the wrong route (e.g., intravenously instead of by intramuscular injection or by mouth) or in the wrong site (e.g., on the right foot instead of the left). (Getting a drug earlier or later than the doctor ordered is not considered an error.) The effect of a particular medication error can range from essentially zero to death, depending on the characteristics of the drug and the condition of the patient. (One study found that 11 percent of malpractice claims resulting in payment involved treatment with drugs but did not distinguish between erroneous treatment and the side effects of intended treatment.[35])

The potential for medication error begins with that doctor's order book (or a special order form for medications), in which the name of the drug may be not quite legible; the dosage, if legible, may be wrong or may be omitted; and the route of administration may similarly be misstated or forgotten. If the order were given as part of a conversation between doctor and nurse, it would not take a major initiative for the nurse to obtain what information was omitted or to clarify what was illegible or otherwise questionable. Once the doctor has scribbled his orders and left the scene, however, it is appreciably easier for the nurse or the pharmacist to guess at his intentions than it is to track him down and risk his resenting that his authority appears to be in question. And if the nurse administering the medication had had a chance to become familiar with the patient and his condition, her guess would more likely be an accurate one; she would be unlikely, for example, to administer the patient's ear drops in his eyes, because what had been written as "A.U." (both ears) looked to her like "O.U." (each eye).[36]

Or if the nurses' work encouraged them to relate to patients as individuals rather than as diseases parked in particular locations, they would be less likely to commit the kind of error in which medication intended for the patient who had been in bed A is administered to the patient who is *now* in bed A. That plastic bracelet is intended to preclude such mishaps, but it isn't always consulted and it's sometimes removed during a diagnostic procedure.[37]

Or if nursing work were divided by patient rather than by task, a patient would be less likely to get duplicate medication because both a senior floor nurse and a nurse being oriented thought they were responsible for administering it. (The first neglected to record the dosage, as procedure required.) [38] There are always procedural regulations drawn up in the most minute detail that are advertised, and justified, as precluding medication errors and related mishaps, but there are always people working in hospitals who understandably do not delight in concentrating on such minutiae or who are subject to being distracted by more interesting concerns.[39]

Some types of medication error can hardly be blamed on the organization of hospital work, but at the same time could never have happened were the patient being treated at home. In this category is the case in which the nurse was on the way to administer the proper medication to the proper patient, but the patient started slipping out of bed; the nurse put his three drug doses on his roommate's nightstand to help him up, and his roommate consumed the medication before the nurse realized what was happening.[40]

The same caste-ridden fragmentation that facilitates medication errors makes it unlikely that they will be subject to the kind of in-hospital discussion that might improve the odds against their happening. As expressed in a journal for hospital pharmacists, "Every group of professionals and every department is vulnerable. If you are inclined to point the finger at another professional or department, you soon find yourself on the spot with the next incident." [41]

Medication errors are not of course the most significant risks to which a hospital patient is subject. His greatest risks are inherent in the types of procedures, primarily surgical and diagnostic, for which the hospital provides the setting; these deserve a chapter to themselves, which follows this one. But there is a risk that results from the hospital itself as a unique kind of enclosed space, the risk of hospital-acquired, or nosocomial, infection.

The biology of nosocomial infections, crudely put, reflects the hospital as an environment for an assortment of microbes—originating in patients, workers, visitors, and various others—whose potential for harm is exacerbated by the presence of antibiotics, which spurs them on to evolve into antibiotic-resistant strains. This mix surrounds a population—the sick (especially the elderly and those with surgical wounds) and the newborn—that by definition has a low resistance to infection. Over time, of course, the use of antibiotics (introduced in the 1940's) has soared, and hospital populations have come to be older and more severely ill. What all this means is that, from the point of view of infection, the people in a hospital would be exposed to an enormously smaller degree of biological risk were they at home getting well; indeed, one legal treatise for hospital administrators maintains that "the general public is considered to know that hospitals are places where one would expect to encounter such [infectious and contagious] diseases." [42]

That risk comes to fruition with the in-hospital infection of about 5 percent of patients, as estimated by the Center for Disease Control.[43] Other studies have reported rates as high as 13 percent,[44] and all studies are subject to the occasional difficulty of distinguishing between an infection acquired in the hospital and one brought in from the outside world, not to mention the psychological incentive to underdetection. Only about 2.5 percent of malpractice cases focus on nosocomial infections per se,[45] probably because it can be excruciatingly difficult to meet a standard of proof requiring that one know how the infection was acquired and then demonstrate that some hospital functionary was negligent and that this negligence was the cause of the infection.[46]

Hospitals have reacted to the problem of their generating infections by elaborating on their already convoluted bureaucracy. The 1960's saw the creation of such new job categories as the infection-control nurse and the hospital epidemiologist,[47] and a hospital is now required to include a multidisciplinary infection-control committee within its structure as a condition of accreditation.[48] These mechanisms may be able to pinpoint such medical disasters as the malfunctioning ventilating system that was sucking into the operating room air that had passed over an open garbage container;[49] they will not, however, be able to eliminate the underlying elements of microbes, antibiotics, and people whose resistance is low. In the words of one book on the subject, "Health facilities will probably never be completely free of infection because they exist to administer [sic] to the ill." [50]

None of the hazards of hospitalization would be relevant to our concerns were there not simultaneously something about hospitalization as a human experience that has the potential to create sufficient anger in the patient for him to seek retaliation if and when one of its risks comes to fruition.[51] It is generally agreed that a person begins a hospitalization (particularly if it is his first, or his first in that hospital) feeling anxious and fearful, and that his anxiety and fear are as much associated with the hospital as with his illness.[52] His fears are then typically exacerbated by what appears to be a conspiracy of hospital functionaries to deny him information, both about himself and about the strange place he finds himself in. Not that he seeks a short course in medicine, only the sort of simple explanations that bring reassurance by dispelling irrational imaginings or the even simpler prior announcements of coming events that dispel fear of the unknown and allow time for psychological preparation. Doctors and nurses, however, either fail to see or choose to ignore these needs, letting fear blossom into helplessness and a feeling of abandonment sometimes verging on panic.[53]

The patient's fears come to include a fear of communicating with hospital functionaries, who have made it absolutely clear that fulfilling his obligation to be a "good patient" precludes anything other than a posture of passive acceptance. They have also made clear the patient's dependence on their good graces—" 'It doesn't pay to make enemies anywhere. If they see their button light up, they could just keep you waiting.' " [54] The patient's fear of communicating not only makes him reluctant to seek reassurance but also inhibits his passing on information about his condition or suspicions that something is amiss; the one who got his ear drops in his eyes, for example, accepted that fact without complaint.[55] Thus, the patient, unawares, becomes

a part of the risk system of hospital misorientation and a
conspirator against his own interests. (Occasionally a person
becomes aware that this is his situation, as in the case of one
patient quoted, after his discharge from a "highly rated institution," as saying: " 'I was glad to get out; a hospital is
no place for a sick man. When you are in a hospital, you
should be able to *defend* yourself.' " [56])

As it increases risk, the communications void simultaneously increases distrust. Patients associate medical competence with a physician's openness: "I think doctors should
tell patients the truth, because I think that builds a lot of
confidence.' " [57] Without openness, suspicion is only intensified: "the newly admitted patient . . . was cautious in
accepting what he was told about his illness because he
came to the hospital suspecting that physicians lie to patients, and his experiences in the hospital reinforced this
suspicion." [58]

Patient resentment—usually unexpressed at the time or
else shifted to a safe target, such as the food—then becomes
the typical reaction to the experience of being hospitalized.
Resentment may develop in somewhat different ways, depending on the patient's personality. Some will resent their
loss of independence from the beginning, feeling it an affront
to their adulthood; others will initially enjoy being passive
but will become resentful when they discover that the
hospital's willingness to care for their illness does not extend
to the family or financial problems that go with it.[59] Then
they join the first group in resenting the hospital's denial of
their unique humanity and their transmutation into mere
specimens of a classification of disease.

If the operation is a success or the wonder drug works its
advertised wonders, resentment will probably more or less
dissipate as the patient rejoins the world of the well. If, however, the patient feels less than his former self after emerging from the hospital's clutches, all the slights and indignities he has suffered at its hands will emerge from memory,

like the genie from the lamp, and fear and resentment will work their transformation into anger pure and simple. "Interviews with patients who had sued often revealed that the suing patient had become angry in the hospital because of the way he . . . had been treated by nurses or admissions office personnel. . . . In many cases the bad experiences they reported were interpersonal ones (as opposed to strictly medical or surgical actions), or . . . complaints over the absence of interpersonal experiences. The patients did not like to be neglected." [60] The doctor may even have been a more or less innocent bystander to these slights and indignities, but it was the doctor, after all, who had the patient hospitalized, and it will probably be the doctor who becomes the focus of the patient's anger.

3

The Tools of Modern Medical Practice

If someone died while being Intensively Cared for, he automatically set off a siren that screamed all over the building. The system was attached to each bed and wired ingeniously to the patient's vital organs, so that he had absolutely no way of dying peacefully in his sleep. All departures were piercingly announced in the lobby, elevators, ladies' rooms, staff cafeteria and gift shoppe. Every doctor in the house came for the send-off. One squeak of that signal and they were hurtling through the halls like a pack of dissident white mice taking over Pavlov's maze. And then, from behind the swinging doors, you could hear this anvil chorus of bare fists thwacking on a bare chest. Whoever it was wasn't dead until the fists stopped.

LOIS GOULD, *Such Good Friends*

We are now in an era of high technology in which medical injury is a risk that must be accepted either in the practice of medicine or in the conduct of hospitalization.

WILLIAM J. McGILL, President, Columbia University, and Chairman, New York State Special Advisory Panel on Medical Malpractice

AN orthopedic surgeon was bemoaning, and attempting to explain, the special impact the malpractice crisis had had on practitioners of his specialty: "Orthopedists are carrying out procedures today that twenty years ago would have been impossible. People would have been doomed to wheelchairs and are no longer so. But there is a risk when you replace a joint with artificial materials. There is a risk of rejection. There is a risk of infection, and the patients have to understand that they must accept part of the responsibility for that risk." [1]

Ignoring the sermonizing that concludes this statement, we must grant that the rest of it makes an important point, a point not limited to orthopedists. The same conjunction of technological advance and risk is equally present when a cardiac surgeon implants a pacemaker, when a gastroenterologist performs a liver biopsy, or when a general practitioner prescribes an antibiotic. Just as the risk of indigestion inheres in a Thanksgiving dinner, so the risk of greater or lesser physical harm inheres in the harvest of medical progress.

The hallmark of modern medical practice is technology— a variously defined concept that is used here to encompass the fallout from medicine's scientific pretensions, whether a piece of equipment priced in six figures, a sophisticated surgical or diagnostic procedure, or a selection from among the enormous array of possibilities that medical people call chemotherapy and that most of us call drugs. In the pretechnological era of medical practice, people were commonly confronted with prolonged illness or death because, as the doctor would patiently explain, "There's nothing medicine can do." When medicine had few pretensions, there were equally few opportunities for blaming one's miseries on medical practice. When, however, there is much that medicine can and does do, both the risks and the opportunities for blame multiply accordingly. There are the risks inherent in particular technological maneuvers, whatever the expertise of the practitioner; there are the risks created when the practitioner executes a particular technological maneuver with less than optimal judgment or skill; and there are the risks of the practitioner's neglecting to perform a particular technological maneuver, as when a condition goes undiagnosed and therefore untreated because he failed to employ a tool of modern medical diagnosis. All these risks, when they are realized in the form of identifiable harm to the patient, are potential sources of blame directed at medicine and its practitioners.

The likelihood that blame will be forthcoming is then magnified by the fact that as medical technology increases risk, it simultaneously increases the psychological distance between doctor and patient and the imposed passivity of the patient. As the doctor retreats further into his scientific cocoon, his words and actions become less and less comprehensible to the patient, while at the same time the patient's words and actions become less and less important to the doctor's diagnosis and treatment of his condition. Taking a history and performing a physical examination, which classically have been the basis of medical diagnosis and which require direct doctor-patient contact and the active cooperation of the patient, have steadily declined in importance relative to a growing array of diagnostic procedures that develop detached, objectified evidence of pathology. These typically involve the patient only in the minimal, passive contact of offering his body up to nurses and technicians while they extract from it blood, X-ray pictures, or squiggles on a graph.

The clinical laboratory, for example, where automation began to be introduced in the late 1950's, has become one of the most technologically advanced aspects of modern medical practice. (Now one piece of automatic, computerized equipment can perform twenty tests on a single blood sample.) Not to let such impressive technology go to waste, American medical practice produced roughly 3 billion lab tests in 1971, a figure that climbed to about 5 billion in 1975.[2] Back in 1951, the number of tests performed on a routine maternity patient was about five; by 1971, it had become about fourteen. For a patient with a perforated appendix the increment was from five to thirty-one.[3] (The proponents of automatic lab equipment point to the significant decrease in cost per test it effects; with the increase it inspires in the number of tests ordered per patient, however, the total lab cost per patient typically rises.[4])

One professional appraisal of medicine's growing passion for the products of the laboratory is a diagnosis of "serendipitomania, the common habit of ordering all the laboratory tests in hopes of 'falling into' a disease." This condition was found to encompass a class of "laboratory-error syndromes," which "are probably the most responsive to treatment of all entities—one merely has to repeat the test once or twice to see astounding results." [5]

In a less lighthearted vein, there is the general observation that so-called normal laboratory values vary with the patient's age, sex, time of day, whether or not he has recently eaten, within an individual over time, and between laboratories.[6] Or there is, for example, the sobering story of a particular clinical conference discussing the case of a particular dead patient:

> The presentation included laboratory data covering a large blackboard. The patient had died without a definite diagnosis after very careful study by well-informed and intelligent young people. To several physicians who were attending the conference and who had not attempted to evaluate the profusion of laboratory tests, the history, physical findings and course of illness appeared to point clearly to liver abscess, and the post-mortem examination showed that there was indeed such an abscess, resulting from pylephlebitis [inflammation of the portal vein, which brings blood from the intestines to the liver]. Possibly, an early and correct diagnosis would have resulted in successful treatment.[7]

Technological advance, in other words, is not automatically equivalent to superior wisdom or efficacy. "Much of the preference for the new, more complicated, more expensive procedures comes about not because medical knowledge has grown so much, but because it has grown so little. In many cases it is thought that one procedure is superior (in a purely technological sense) to another, but what one would really like to know is *how much* superior it is in terms of *end results*." [8] The "technologic imperative" [9] that propels medical practice, as it propels other sectors of American society, means that "procedures get done because we have the capability. We build a new machine because the technology is there, but it really doesn't add anything to what we can do for the patient." [10] This tendency is but one reflection of the fact that, like other important actors on the American scene, the doctor is trained and expected to be an activist, to engage in active intervention rather than passive observation. [11] "Given the choice of administering or withholding therapy, the American physician appears likely to choose active therapy." [12]

The American doctor's choice of possible therapies has ballooned in the period since World War II, a period when most of what we think of as scientific medicine has come into use and when American medicine (replacing German) has taken a position of global dominance. (As we saw in the previous chapter, the postwar period has also brought us the additional hospital space needed to carry out the new therapies and, as we shall find in the chapter that follows, it further has seen the emergence of medical specialization as the dominant means of delivering the new therapies.)

Like the postwar boom in hospital construction, the medical technological explosion was largely underwritten with federal money. Perhaps it was an attempt to replicate in another field the wartime experience of performing impressive technological feats by spending massive amounts of money. Unexpended wartime biomedical research grants were placed under the jurisdiction of the National Institutes of Health, and to quote the recollections of one academic physician, "We in the medical schools found an abundance of money available for research. We 'tooled up' rapidly, building and equipping laboratories, recruiting supporting staff, and organizing training programs for future research workers." [13] The NIH budget of $2.5 million in 1945 swelled to $285 million in 1960 and $1.6 billion in 1970, and "by 1960 the medical schools had become in large part arms or branches of NIH." [14] Expenditures for medical research from all sources (excluding money spent by drug and medical-equipment companies) erupted from $110 million ($.72 per capita) in 1950 to $592 million ($3.21 per capita) in 1960 to $1.8 billion ($8.90 per capita) in 1970.[15]

The fact that the research dollars flowed to investigators located at medical schools (in part as a means of circumventing the American Medical Association's opposition to federal aid to medical education as such) meant that medical-school faculties came increasingly to comprise physicians who were scientific researchers as much as, if not more than, they were practitioners of medicine. The role models then presented to successive waves of medical students increasingly came to be people who saw and projected themselves as scientists more than as healers. At the same time the affluence and prestige surrounding the academic-scientific model made it increasingly appealing to hospitals, and the proportion of them affiliated with a medical school grew from 5.6 percent in 1960 to 12.2 percent in 1973.[16] (Teaching hospitals tending to be larger than average, the percentage of total beds represented by those figures is appreciably higher.)

The biomedical research bonanza started to lose steam in the mid-1960's, but by then the content of medical practice and the distribution of disease had undergone significant alteration. Penicillin (first generally available in 1945) and succeeding generations of antibiotics were keeping infectious-disease patients either out of the hospital altogether or there for much shorter periods of time, and the polio vaccine (first introduced in 1955) had shut down the polio wards and their cumbersome iron lungs. In place of such patients were the growing numbers suffering from less tractable chronic or degenerative conditions, who became candidates for such achievements of the new technology as coronary-care units, cardiac surgery, cancer chemotherapy or radiation therapy, and artificial joints or kidneys.[17] One reflection of the shift was the new hardware in the hospital— postoperative recovery rooms were to be found in only about 30 percent of hospitals in 1955, but in 83 percent in 1975; electroencephalography in about 12 percent in 1955, in 47 percent in 1975; intensive-care units in less than 10 percent in 1955, in 69 percent in 1975; and so on.[18]

Not that the development of technological medicine has been onward and upward in an unbroken line; its innovators and their followers have been subject to repeated attacks of what might be called chronic medical faddism. The course of this condition involves a new technological innovation catching on (sometimes immediately, sometimes more gradually) to the point where it is employed on every remotely applicable occasion, until second thoughts set in and its use drastically declines, sometimes to the point of oblivion, more commonly to a much more circumscribed role in the medical repertory, possibly in favor of a still newer technique.[19] As two business-administration academics explain it: "For medical services, the life cycle [of a new technology] typically stops short of complete development. . . . The entire industry is structured for innovation so that new services are continually obsoleting [sic] prior ones before they become highly mature." [20] Or in the words of two clinicians: "A bold new diagnostic procedure may be developed, disseminated, modified, displaced, and discarded in less than a decade; it will run the full gamut from enthusiastic application to stigmatized obsolescence." [21]

Thus, for example, dicoumarol, an oral anticoagulant drug (inhibiting the formation of blood clots), was first used experimentally in 1948 in the treatment of people who had had heart attacks, and the trials being deemed successful, its use as long-term therapy rapidly became almost universal. Later clinical trials, however, brought its long-term effectiveness into serious question, and it was eventually accepted as beneficial in the prevention of strokes for only a short period following a heart attack.[22] Gastric freezing as a treatment for ulcers was introduced in 1962; by 1964 there were 1,000 gastric freezing machines in use in the United States; there were 2,500 by 1969. The same year brought publication of the results of a large-scale, carefully controlled clinical study, showing definitively that gastric freezing was no more effective than no treatment at all. The procedure went out of vogue very quickly.[23] Tonsillectomies were routinely performed on children for decades, but have since come to be considered, at least by academic physicians, to be of value only rarely.[24] Hyperbaric chambers for performing surgery (at $100,000 per installation) were the rage in the 1960's, but have since come to be viewed as having only marginal benefit.[25] The use of drugs to treat mild hypertension is a vogue of the seventies that has increasingly been called into question.[26]

All of these examples of medical faddism—and the many more that could be mentioned—have in common the creation of greater or lesser risk to the patient at a time when the benefit of the new procedure, and whether that benefit can be confidently said to justify its risk, has not been firmly established. The underlying bias of the technological mindset and its activist orientation assumes that newer must be better and that doing more must be better than doing less; hence, the possibility of harm is always a second thought, and one that is only reluctantly entertained.

To trace the course of risk and potential anger through the entire maze of technological medical procedures would require an encyclopedia.[27] The point can be made and most of its ramifications accounted for by taking a general look at diagnostic procedures, drugs, and surgery. In each of these areas, however, the data on risk, as manifested in adverse effects, are at best random and incomplete. The initial, and most obvious, problem is that medical science has not created anything resembling a mechanism for the systematic collection of data on any aspect of iatrogenic illness. ("Iatros" being Greek for doctor, iatrogenic illness is literally doctor-caused illness, but the term has come to stand for a broader concept encompassing adverse effects of medical treatment whether or not the doctor is directly implicated.)

The more subtle problem is that even studies of adverse effects conducted in particular settings and at particular times are not guaranteed to discover all such effects. One such study, for example, acknowledged that some "episodes" were discovered essentially fortuitously, "because the patient mentioned it to other patients or to ward attendants, or because the physician accidentally encountered information in the nurses' notes or overheard their oral reports." The report went on to acknowledge the possibility that some iatrogenesis was not detected because it did not become manifest until after the patient had been discharged from the hospital.[28] When detection is not always easy, the natural bias toward underdetection on the part of those conducting the study can easily come into play. And, finally, studies of iatrogenesis typically exclude cases of error and negligence from their scope, which is useful for the purpose of looking at the magnitude of risk inherent in even the most competent medical care but is not useful for determining the magnitude of risk to which patients in the real world are subjected.

The process of medical diagnosis used to find the physician positioned safely beyond the outer borders of his patient's body, there to deduce the nature of its internal processes by looking, listening, kneading, thumping, and manipulating. But the "rapid expansion of the sciences of diagnosis" has brought us "an impressive array of diagnostic procedures that violate, almost with impunity, the internal environment of the human organism." [29] Beyond the hardware for collecting blood to feed the voracious appetite of the clinical labs, there are the biopsy needles to extract pieces of organs such as liver and kidney, the centesis needles to draw fluid from spaces such as the spinal canal and chest cavity, the endoscopes to insert into bodily openings and peer into such organs as stomach and rectum, the radiopaque substances to inject into blood vessels and cavities to permit X-ray visualization of assorted parts of the anatomy. "But each new diagnostic technic that requires invasion of the body carries a potential for pathology. Often this is not anticipated or fully appreciated until a new iatrogenic disease has been established clinically, its natural history defined, and the spectrum of manifestations recorded." [30]

Needles may introduce infection, cause hemorrhage, or miss the intended organ and puncture another; endoscopes may perforate the bodily tube into which they are inserted. And as for those radiopaque substances, "All contrast media are toxic, some more than others. . . . More frequent and more intensive application of contrast media to the medical problems of patients has resulted in an absolute increase in the number of complications." [31]

The risk is not limited to what inheres in the procedure itself, but encompasses as well the risk from drugs used as "premedication"—something to anesthetize the windpipe before inserting a bronchoscope down it, for example. And the risk is multiplied when the patient, as is frequently the case, becomes the object of a whole smorgasbord of procedures and their attendant drugs.

Remembering that such data are no more than impressionistic, we might note one study of iatrogenic "episodes" striking patients on the medical service of a prestigious teaching hospital, which found that 29 of the 198 patients so afflicted (14.6 percent) had experienced adverse reactions to diagnostic procedures or drugs used for diagnostic purposes. (The 198 victims of iatrogenesis represented 20 percent of admissions during the study period.) Two deaths were directly attributed to diagnostic procedures (one cystoscopic examination and one thoracentesis), and in three other cases of death a diagnostic procedure was felt to be the precipitating cause (one esophagoscopy and two barium enemas).[32]

Once the diagnostic stage has been passed, with or without mishap and with or without a definitive diagnosis having been established, the strategy of treatment * undertaken, whatever else it involves, is more than likely to include the administration of medication. In 1900 the physician's pharmacopoeia (excluding snake oil) comprised about six substances (digitalis, morphine, quinine, diphtheria antitoxin, aspirin, and ether; immunization was also available against smallpox and rabies).[33] In 1972 the American physician had about 6,780 single drug entities to choose from, not to mention 3,330 combination products, all of which were available in 14,250 different dosage forms and strengths.[34] Of the two hundred drug products he prescribed most frequently in 1969, five had been introduced during the entire nineteenth century, fourteen between 1900 and 1940, eighteen in the 1940's, ninety-five in the 1950's, and sixty-six in the 1960's.[35]

And the American doctor has been prescribing with a vengeance; in 1972 an estimated 1,161 million prescriptions were filled by community pharmacies, 174 million by pharmacies in department stores, supermarkets, and discount stores, 108 million by dispensing physicians, and 938 million by hospital pharmacies (732 million for inpatients and 186 million for outpatients)—which gives us the staggering total of 2,381 million (or about 2.4 billion), or about 11.6 per capita. The 5.5 prescriptions per capita dispensed that year by community pharmacies alone was more than double the 2.4 per capita they dispensed in 1950.[36] By the mid-seventies three-quarters of visits to general practitioners, internists, and family practitioners were being concluded with the doctor prescribing at least one drug.[37]

---

* An outsider is struck by the militaristic terminology that pervades the medical literature, where strategies, maneuvers, and interventions abound. One cannot help but wonder whether the body is in danger of becoming a battleground like that Vietnamese village of which it was said that we destroyed it in order to save it.

That drug was frequently one of those postwar miracles, the antibiotics, which account for 15 to 20 percent of all prescriptions in community practice [38] and are prescribed for 20 to 40 percent of hospitalized patients, depending on the season.[39] The use of antibiotics rose by about 30 percent in the period 1964 to 1971, although the growth in population and in visits to doctors was only about 5 percent.[40]

Introducing the chemistry of medication into an individual's internal ecology is intrinsically risky. Drugs (even aspirin) are inherently toxic and, at dosage levels that vary widely among individuals, will produce a toxic reaction. And practically any drug will in some people produce a hypersensitivity, or allergic, reaction, a danger that is unpredictable unless the reaction has occurred before. Either type of reaction may be as trivial as a transient skin rash, as final as death. If the drug is injected, there is an intensified risk from the greater concentration and more sudden introduction of the drug, and the additional risk of infection from unsterile equipment or improper cleansing of the skin. If the drug is given in the form of intravenous fluid, there is the risk of death from pulmonary edema (filling up of the lungs with fluid) and the risk of a wide variety of lesser complications from such a drastic alteration of the individual's internal chemical environment.[41]

Adverse reactions to drugs, whatever the particular causation, "may spare a patient's life but leave him blind or deaf, afflicted with kidney, liver or brain damage, bone necrosis, ulceration of the bowel, intestinal hemorrhage, skin scars, extreme sensitivity to sunlight, or other disabilities that may last for months or years." [42] Hospitalized patients are especially vulnerable, partly because they are relatively older and sicker than other patients, partly because they are made to consume a larger number of drugs during their illness.[43]

Polypharmacy—the prescribing of multiple medications —creates a risk that is greater than the sum of risks from the individual drugs, because the chemistry of their interactions creates new dangers. Combining an anticoagulant with an antiarthritic drug, for example, may cause serious or fatal hemorrhaging because the latter has a potentiating effect on the former. Conversely, the effect of tetracycline (an antibiotic) is nullified if the patient is also taking an antacid that contains calcium, magnesium, or aluminum, because these metallic substances block the absorption of the tetracycline.[44]

Those medical favorites, the antibiotics, represent a notably pernicious situation of risk, one that usually comes to fruition when the antibiotic is given, as it is called, prophylactically—to a patient with a viral infection (against which antibiotics are ineffective) to "prevent" a complicating bacterial infection, or to a surgical patient to "prevent" a wound infection. In such cases the antibiotic may do its destructive work against harmless bacteria that were preserving the patient's internal ecological balance by keeping in check other, less benign, bacteria or fungi; these then become free to multiply and prosper, possibly giving the patient what is known as a superinfection, which itself may well be resistant to antibiotics.[45] In this way, antibiotic therapy "may convert a benign self-limited disease into one that may become serious and prolonged—often fatal." [46]

But even when given appropriately, antibiotics "have directly led to kidney, gastrointestinal, pulmonary, liver, and nervous system destruction, and to disfiguring, disabling, and sometimes lethal skin reactions. They have injured the bone marrow . . . and have caused aplastic anemia, agranulocytosis, hemolytic anemia, and other blood dyscrasias, which sometimes are fatally irreversible. They have triggered serious anaphylactic or other allergic responses, including asthma, serum sickness, and skin disorders." [47]

As the thalidomide disaster of the early 1960's made most people aware, pregnant women and the fetuses they carry represent a class of patients especially vulnerable to drug-induced injury. (Thalidomide was in widespread use in Europe as a mild sedative and hypnotic from 1959 to 1962; it was eventually implicated in the deformity of an estimated 3,000 living children in West Germany alone.) A number of drugs if taken by a pregnant woman can cause miscarriage, fetal or neonatal death, or a wide variety of abnormalities or diseases in the infant.[48]

The general problem this unpleasant disquisition is addressing has very little to do with whether the Food and Drug Administration is or is not sufficiently vigilant or whether the profit motive does or does not induce the pharmaceutical industry to attempt to market unsafe drugs. Any drug therapy, however relatively safe the medication and however apparently appropriate its administration, involves some measure of risk. And collective risk increases over time with the increase in the number of people being medicated, the number of products available for that purpose, and the tendency to equate medical care with taking medicine.

Although, as we noted earlier, fully reliable and generalizable quantifications of that risk do not exist, it may be useful to mention in passing the results of a few studies of adverse drug reactions. The Boston Collaborative Drug Surveillance Program has surveyed the most adverse of drug reactions, namely, death; it monitored 26,462 patients treated on the medical (as opposed to surgical, etc.) services of twenty-one acute disease hospitals in seven countries (ten in the United States) from 1971 to 1976. Of these there were 24 deaths, or 0.9 per thousand patients, in which both the attending physician and the clinical pharmacology unit agreed that a drug or drugs administered during hospitalization had definitely or most probably been the major cause of death. Of the seven countries involved, the United States had the second-highest death rate, 1.2 per thousand (behind New Zealand, with a rate of 1.4 per thousand).[49]

A study limited to one hospital but including less catastrophic drug reactions monitored 1,252 admissions to the Yale University Medical Service of Grace-New Haven Community Hospital and sought to record every "noxious response to medical care." (The results of "inadvertent errors" by doctors and nurses were excluded.) Half of the iatrogenic "episodes" detected (119 of 240) were adverse reactions to therapeutic (as opposed to diagnostic) drugs; these afflicted 9.5 percent of admissions. Of the 119 reactions, 58 were classified as either major or moderate; the 11 major reactions included four fatal toxic reactions.[50]

A study of 240 patients at North Carolina Memorial Hospital also found that roughly half the untoward reactions to treatment comprised adverse effects of drugs administered in the hospital. Of sixty-three episodes, twenty-eight (45 percent) were drug reactions (affecting 11.7 percent of the patients), of which fifteen were considered moderate or major.[51] Other studies of hospitalized medical patients have found that from 10 to 18 percent of them suffered adverse drug reactions.[52]

Then there is the situation in which hospitalization is required because of the effects of drugs taken outside the hospital. A study of that phenomenon at the University of Florida Teaching Hospital found that 2.9 percent of medical admissions over a three-year period (177 of 6,063) were due to drug-induced illness, which in about one-third of the cases involved two or more medications.[53] Other studies of hospital admissions reflecting drug-induced disease show admission rates ranging from 1.7 to 4.5 percent.[54]

The phenomenon of chronic medical faddism touches drug use as much as any other aspect of medical practice, perhaps more. As with thalidomide, a drug may be widely consumed for extended periods before the extent of its adverse effects becomes apparent. And most such effects are less bizarre than the deformities of the thalidomide children, which means that the concentrated medical attention required to correlate a given effect with administration of a specific drug will come about only with much greater difficulty, if at all.

The most widespread objects of medical faddism are undoubtedly the antibiotics. Irrational yet common practices involving antibiotics include prescribing an antibiotic for a viral illness, prescribing an antibiotic without taking a culture, prescribing an antibiotic by telephone without examining the patient, and prescribing an antibiotic prophylactically when the efficacy of such prophylaxis is dubious. One antibiotic, chloramphenicol, continued to be prescribed for trivial conditions long after there had been ample documentation that it could cause aplastic anemia, which is usually fatal.[55]

Irrational prescribing of antibiotics is but a common example of the doctor as activist-technologist, expected by himself and his society to act upon his patient's body rather than to teach the patient how to give his body's intrinsic healing powers a chance to act. Writing a prescription, because it is something that only a physician can legally do, gives him psychological satisfaction as an exercise of his unique power, and receiving a prescription gives the patient psychological satisfaction as a gift of that unique power: "In our society, the physician validates his power by prescribing medication, just as a shaman in a primitive tribe may validate his by spitting out a bit of bloodstained down at the proper moment." [56]

But the prescription, a thing, easily comes to substitute for the dialogue, the relationship, that might have made it unnecessary. "Rather than spend the time to explain the natural course of self-limited disease and to reassure the patient, the busy physician 'cops out' with his prescription pad." [57] Or in the hospital setting, "Sedatives may be requested on the days that the physician fails to visit the patient who is recovering, say, from a myocardial infarction. In this instance the sedative serves to muffle the anxiety that would have been precluded, or at least minimized, by the support and reassurance usually provided by the physician." [58] The assumption that physicians usually provide support and reassurance to their hospitalized patients is questionable, as we have seen, but the point is nonetheless valid that drugs are used to fill a void left by a lack of human relatedness.

Patient and physician typically collude in the substitution of the drug for the relationship; after all, they are both part of "a society where consumption of commodities is very generally promoted as a source of happiness and accepted as a substitute for social and psychological satisfactions in work, family, and social contexts." [59] More particularly, the patient is part of "a public incessantly encouraged to gobble or to apply some special brand of [over-the-counter] medication for every conceivable ache or distress," [60] while the physician is part of a subculture in which maximizing the number of patients he sees is the socially accepted route to a yacht and a country estate, and wielding his prescription pad with a professional flourish is an appreciably more efficient means to that end than attempting to talk things out. [61]

Just as the doctor's repertory of drugs to prescribe has expanded enormously in the postwar period, so has the profession's repertory of surgical procedures, in part because the availability of antibiotics has made the danger of wound infection less of a deterrent to operate. "Surgical procedures have become increasingly complex, more definitive, of longer duration and of greater hazard to the patient. Surgeons are willing to operate upon patients at either extreme of life, upon patients in the poorest physical condition and even with small prospect for success." [62] The product of modern surgical practice can walk around with an artificial hip and someone else's kidney, while his heartbeat is prompted by a battery-powered pacemaker. One classification of surgical procedures lists almost a thousand. [63]

In 1949, when the American population numbered 148 million, about 9 million surgical operations were performed;

in 1975 there were 20 million operations for a population of 211 million. The number of operations performed, in other words, had increased 122 percent, while the population had increased but 43 percent, or, if you prefer, the rate of operations had risen from 61 per 1,000 population to 95.[64]

While surgical specialties represent about 30 percent of all physicians [65] and surgical patients represent about 40 percent of all hospital admissions,[66] surgical mishaps represent about 60 percent of all malpractice claims.[67] This does not imply that surgeons bungle more frequently than their colleagues in other specialties. It does imply that their work, whether bungled or not, places its object, the patient, under greater and more obvious risk than the work of their non-surgical colleagues, and also that their manner of functioning is perhaps more likely to evoke anger if and when their work is less than fully successful.

The mortality rate from surgery is something like 1.4 percent for all operations; [68] 0.5 percent is "commonly regarded as the irreducible mortality of surgery." [69] Death may stem from cardiac arrest, which in turn may reflect the administration of anesthesia rather than the surgery proper. (A study of forty-one malpractice suits involving cardiac arrest during anesthesia and surgery found the probable cause of nine, or 22 percent, of the arrests was a major deviation from accepted anesthetic practice.[70]) Or cardiac arrest may leave the patient alive but with an irreversibly damaged brain (as happened to eleven of the forty-one cases, representing all but three of the survivors).

The mortality rate associated with a particular operation may be minuscule, but the operation may be so common that the rate produces a significant number of deaths. The mortality rate for tonsillectomy, for example, is only about one per thousand patients (0.1 percent), but in the United States that translates into 100 to 300 deaths a year.[71] And while the riskiness of the surgery increases with the complexity of the procedure and the relatively poor health of the patient, a routine operation undergone while in good health is not guaranteed against mishap (that study of cardiac arrests found that they "occurred frequently in patients of good health who were having relatively routine surgical procedures").

Something like 30 to 60 percent of patients having general surgical operations experience deep vein thrombosis (formation of a blood clot),[72] which carries the risk of death from pulmonary embolism (the clot traveling to, and lodging in, the lung). And something like 2 to 6 percent of patients undergoing so-called clean surgical procedures develop wound infections, despite the painstaking aseptic precautions that attend modern surgical practice.[73] This is one area where the so-called prophylactic use of antibiotics can have a boomerang effect: "The routine use of antibiotics in the preoperative and postoperative care of patients undergoing 'clean' surgery has resulted in an increased incidence of postoperative infection due to resistant staphylococci." [74] One study of iatrogenic injuries among hospitalized medical, surgical, and gynecological patients found that 65 percent of the injuries detected constituted postoperative complications and that half of these were infections.[75]

The situation of surgery is the quintessence of medical activism: "In general it is clear that there tends to be a bias in favor of operating. After all, the surgeon is trained to operate, he feels active, useful, effective when he is operating. For the patient and his family, in their state of anxiety and tension also, inactivity, just waiting to see how things develop, is particularly hard to bear." [76] The situation is also particularly conducive to faddism: "Surgical therapies are extremely difficult to validate; an innovation can therefore gain quite a foothold before suspicion of its inadequacies becomes prevalent. . . . Virtually all cardiac surgery, gastric surgery, and lung surgery are performed on conditions in which the initial surgical procedure can be shown to produce some tangible effects, but the overall success or failure of the intervention cannot really be judged until the patient's status some months later can be determined." [77] Tonsillectomy is the most obvious example of surgical faddism, the peculiarly American penchant for radical mastectomy (as opposed to less drastic surgical treatment of breast cancer) is probably another, and some argue that the latest such vogue is represented by coronary artery bypass surgery. [78]

The surgeon's particular vulnerability to charges of malpractice reflects the intrinsic risks of serious injury his patients face, combined with the likelihood of their feeling angry should he fail to deal with the psychological strains unique to the experience of undergoing surgery. The surgical patient finds himself having to "submit passively to an assault upon his person that is both harmful as well as helpful." He faces the possibility of death, however remote, with the anxieties and fantasies that thoughts of death provoke, and, in the case of some procedures, he grapples with the horror of mutilation and the dread of never again being the same. [79] It is not surprising that surgical patients have been found to be "far more fearful than medical patients." [80]

The surgical patient's pre-existing anxieties are not likely to be relieved by the environment in which he finds himself. "The very setting of surgical procedures, the hospital and the operating room, serve to increase the patient's fears of what will happen to him. The physical setting looks cold, strange, and dangerous. It stimulates the patient's worries about what will be done to him, and how much he may suffer." [81] When the operation is over, the dismal and frustrating situation of any hospitalized patient is made more so for the surgical patient:

Needles are jabbed into the patient's arms; probes, swabs, or drainage tubes are inserted through the nose and down into the throat; evil tasting medicine is poured into his mouth; bed pans are shoved under his buttocks and belatedly removed—these and a variety of other disagreeable demands and indignities are imposed upon him at a time when he is already in a state of general malaise, beset by incision pains, backaches, sore muscles, headaches, distended bowels, constipation, and perhaps a generous spread of angrily itching skin.[82]

And the surgical patient's psychological state has a direct connection with his somatic recovery. In fact, "Experienced surgeons are loath to operate upon patients who present a fixed conviction that they will die from the procedure, for there have been an uncomfortable number of instances in which, despite the absence of discernible causes, such prophecies have come true." [83] States such as "fear, ignorance, apprehension, resentment . . . by reflex action increase postoperative vomiting, urinary retention, lower the threshold to postoperative pain and increase postoperative anorexia [loss of appetite]. . . . The various psychogenic factors which are intimately a part of any surgical disease may thus exert either an unfavorable or a favorable influence upon convalescence, depending to a considerable extent upon the attention and care given to these factors by the surgeon in charge." [84]

The surgeon is in a powerful position to minimize both psychic and somatic problems by providing the patient with explanations, concern, and reassurance before surgery, and warmth and interest afterward. It is most likely, however, that he will appear rushed, unconcerned, and aloof throughout, for he most probably regards the essentials of his work as taking place only when he is assuming an active, decisive stance above a supine, totally passive body, largely concealed by surgical draping, a person reduced to a thing. When that body regains consciousness and begins attempting to function as an active human being, the surgeon will probably continue to concern himself only with its thingness—attending to the state of the wound but hardly noticing the state of the person in whom he created it.[85]

That postoperative "lack of interest by the staff . . . may leave the patient feeling used and exploited. . . . Denial and attempts by the patient to keep from acknowledging his fear and bad feelings toward the surgeon and his staff may become less important should the realization occur that the 'perfect' result was not obtained. The patient may feel that he was misled into expecting more." [86] He may, in other words, become angry.

But the surgeon's focus on the technological, the thingness of medical practice as opposed to the humanness of sickness, is but a refinement of the stance of modern medicine generally. "At the bedside in the presence of a problem [the modern doctor] is less apt to stay and comfort family and patient and more apt to go to the library to see if there is a recent paper that might help with the diagnosis or treatment." [87] While family and patient would probably prefer, and benefit equally from, a doctor's comforting concern, the doctor views the counseling function as either an anachronism or a role to be filled only by psychiatrists. He feels much more comfortable maneuvering the hardware of the modern medical scientist; as one internist said about putting his patients in a coronary-care unit, "With all those monitors and other gadgets, we get a sense of control." [88]

Oddly enough, while the doctor feels he is casting off unscientific superstition, the patient finds a new magic in medical technology, as in the finding of one study that "laboratory tests mystified most patients; the results were viewed as almost uncanny, magical, or superhuman. Some patients thought the tests revealed something very special about them." [89] Or the finding that, among families of dying patients, "the families looked for miracles instead of death. The feeling among laymen was that science and research would bring forth the miracles." [90]

The problem, of course, is that scientific medicine is not only not miraculous but that its apparently magical technology robs the patient of his humanness while it subjects him to iatrogenic risk. Not only is his personhood reduced to a pathological condition, but that condition is then reduced to a computer printout from the lab or a graph from the electrocardiogram. "The patient-as-person has been threatened with extinction by fragmentation, leaving behind him an odd assortment of calibrated readings, metaplastic cells, radioactive isotopes, and several feet of glass tubing, which, assembled in whatever combinations imaginable, fail to add up to a recognizable facsimile of man." [91] Feeling hurt, cheated, and resentful, if and when dehumanization does not result in cure, becomes an almost inevitable reaction.

4

The Agents of Modern
Medical Practice

*I don't like being divided into parts like a machine, one piece
sent here to be fixed and another piece there.*
A patient, quoted in "Humanization and
Dehumanization of Health Care" by Jan Howard

*It's hard to know what to do about a carcinoma that begins on
the lower lid and extends one-half inch below the lid border.*
"One ophthalmologist," quoted in a *Medical Economics*
article on "What's Gone Wrong with Specialization?"

WHERE it used to be "our doctor," it has become our
internist, our pediatrician, our obstetrician-gynecologist, and our allergist, with a surgeon joining the ranks from
time to time, usually on the recommendation of one of the
others. Where in the hospital it used to be "the nurse," it
has become the nurse, the lab technician, the X-ray technician, the dietitian, the respiratory therapist, and the social
worker. Together with the physician or physicians, this agglomeration is proudly called the health-care team, presumably on the theory that passing requisitions, orders, and reports back and forth constitutes teamwork. For the patient,
however, the sporting analogy may have more to do with his
feeling like a bouncing ball that never spends more than a
few seconds in the hands of any one player.

The people who carry out medical treatment ("care" becomes less and less accurate as a description of the process)
have proliferated and become differentiated, both horizontally and vertically. Horizontally, each category of occupation has split into ever more subcategories—nurses, thera-

pists, and technicians, no less than doctors. Vertically, the range of personnel relating to patients has come to extend from the superspecialist doctor with an income in six figures to the lowly attendant with wages in four figures. In 1950 the total of all of them was about 1.7 million people, of whom about 13 percent were physicians; by 1974 the total working in health occupations had grown to about 4.7 million, with physicians comprising less than 8 percent.[1] Of physicians, 36 percent were specialists in 1949, 79 percent in 1974. Surgical specialists, in particular, were 18 percent of physicians in 1949, 32 percent in 1974.[2]

Just as the concentrated development of military technology during World War II provided a catalyst and a model for the postwar boom in biomedical research, so the wartime treatment of physician specialists catalyzed an increase in the proportion of physicians seeking that designation. In the armed forces a general practitioner or uncredentialed specialist was likely to find himself a first lieutenant, while his colleague who had acquired certification by one of the specialty examining boards was made a captain. Those of the former category who got the message conveyed by the ranking system then found a further incentive to pursue specialist status in the federal subsidy of residency training through the GI Bill. As a result, the proportion of the nation's physicians who were in internship and residency programs grew from 6.6 percent in 1940 to 11.4 percent in 1949, the number of approved residencies from about 5,000 in 1940 to over 22,000 in 1952.[3] (In 1974, 17.8 percent of all physicians were in training programs.[4]) The content of that training was substantially influenced by the specialty boards, whose certification was rewarded in the civilian world by higher income and easier access to membership on a hospital's medical staff.[5]

The federal funding of biomedical research reinforced the message that specialized is better. The research fellowships awarded by the various categorical institutes of the

National Institutes of Health spawned a cadre of researcher subspecialists, many of whom went on to apply their sub-specialized training in medical practice: "For the purpose of doing research and investigation, people have to special-ize in some aspect of medicine to narrow the field of study. . . . Pretty soon instead of interns and residents who are generalized in the department of medicine, there are cardiology fellows and cardiology residents, cancer fellows and cancer residents. . . . After training as special-ists, they then all go into practice as specialists." [6]

The structure of the medical-school-affiliated hospitals in which the researchers and trainees were based became ever more splintered: "Some departments of medicine seem al-most like big business conglomerates, in that they consist of many distinct sections, each with its own staff organi-zation." [7] Those who toiled in these heady, hyperspecialized environments became the role models for successive gen-erations of students and trainees. There were no general practitioners to be found in the teaching hospital. [8]

By 1970 there were sixty-three specialties and subspecial-ties recognized by the American Medical Association. [9] Of the certificates awarded by the American Board of Internal Medicine in 1972, 37 percent were subspecialty certificates, representing eight different subspecialties of internal medi-cine. [10] The reward system, whether the Nobel Prize for a researcher or a six-figure income for a superspecialized practitioner, has done its work—a reward system neither created nor administered by patients, however much they find themselves trapped in it and paying for it.

A roughly similar reward system has grown up around nurses, who have discovered that being an angel of mercy or a mother surrogate is less highly rewarded, in income and status, than acquiring pretensions of rationalized pro-fessionalism. Beginning in reaction to their falling wages and general exploitation during the Depression, nurses gradually "began to restructure their idea of what the profession should be. They no longer were content to be seen as primarily the devoted assistants to male professionals. They wanted to be recognized as professionals in their own right. They began to emphasize higher education and technical competence." [11]

With a push from nursing organizations and foundations and the participation of ever larger numbers of universities and community colleges, the traditional training of registered nurses in a three-year hospital-based nursing school is being gradually supplanted by their education in a collegiate setting, from which they emerge with either an associate or, increasingly, a baccalaureate degree. The proportion of R.N.'s produced by hospital-based diploma schools declined from 85 percent of all graduates in 1959 to 31 percent in 1974, while the proportion of nursing graduates receiving B.S.'s rose from 13 percent to 25 percent.[12]

Professionalization has led the registered nurse in one or both of two directions. One direction finds her spending "a large portion of her time being quasi-scientist and ward administrator rather than dispenser of personal care to patients," [13] sitting in the nurse's station relating to pieces of paper rather than hovering at the bedside relating to sick human beings. The other finds her responding to the specialized needs of the increasingly specialized medical profession by becoming a specialist nurse. As of 1976 there were thirteen specialty organizations affiliated with the American Nurses' Association and six specialty certification boards.[14]

As R.N.'s have become more professionalized and therefore more expensive to hire, their primary employers, the hospitals, have stepped up their use of lower-echelon nursing personnel—licensed practical nurses and aides, orderlies, and attendants. Thus, while the number of R.N.'s grew by 117 percent from 1950 to 1973, the number of L.P.N.'s grew by 234 percent and the number of aides, orderlies, and attendants by 312 percent. The proportion of nursing personnel represented by R.N.'s declined in that period from 51 percent to 37 percent, mimicking the decline in the proportion of health workers who are doctors.[15]

While nursing has been professionalizing and differentiating itself, the residual category of health workers, loosely called allied health personnel, has been exploding and fragmenting. (This term is usually used to describe those health occupations remaining after one subtracts doctors, dentists, nurses, pharmacists, and assorted other practitioners such as optometrists and clinical psychologists.) The number in this category increased by 319 percent from 1950 to 1974 (from about 286,200 to about 1,200,000), a period when the number of doctors was increasing by about 65 percent and the number of nursing personnel by about 215 percent.[16] Reflecting the dramatically escalating reliance on the products of the laboratory, the number of clinical lab personnel rose by 475 percent in that period,[17] despite the fact that their equipment was at the same time becoming more and more automated.

Some workers in the allied health classification fill job categories whose existence reflects the development of modern medical technology. Respiratory (formerly inhalation) therapists, for example, of which there were about 18,000 in 1974,[18] were created to operate the increasingly sophisticated breathing equipment first developed in the late 1940's. Hemodialysis technicians became adjuncts of artificial kidneys; nuclear medicine technologists, of scanning devices using isotopes. Other categories, such as clinical dietitian and medical record administrator, reflect the professionalization and differentiation of long-standing functions that are performed in a setting, the hospital, whose organizational structure has become more and more convoluted.

Although other settings employ roughly a third of all health workers, it is the growing importance of the hospital and the increased complexity of what goes on in it that are primarily responsible for the swollen numbers and minute

differentiation of nursing and allied health personnel. Total
hospital employment rose from 1.1 million in 1950 to 2.9
million in 1974;[19] the number of hospital employees per
patient from 1.78 in 1950 to 3.26 in 1974.[20] Whereas the
hospital work force could at one time be divided into doctors, nurses, orderlies, and clerical personnel, a 1974 publication reported that the fragmentation of hospital personnel
had created no fewer than 240 occupational titles to describe them.[21]

Those multitudinous occupational categories, many of
which are not yet well established as essential to the operation of the institution and its therapeutic function, do not
necessarily relate to one another as a harmonious whole:
"A struggle for a place in the hospital sun is unremittingly
waged by most of the myriad occupation groups, especially
those most closely tied to therapeutic tasks. Precisely because systems of authority are unclear, there is often a
premium on flexible, not to say opportunistic, behavior." [22]
The need to establish the importance of one's own occupational group to the therapeutic task may preclude establishing that task itself as one's primary focus: "If the individual
invests so much of himself in a pattern of occupational
loyalty, can he then stretch his identity to embrace other
health workers or the whole medical institution in which
work occurs? Can the individual be dissuaded from considering himself first a physician, nurse, or physical therapist,
and only second, a member of a therapeutic team or of a
hospital-as-society?" [23] Nursing, although one of the oldest
and, in that sense, best established of hospital occupations,
is nonetheless one of the most defensive, for as successive
new categories of technicians, therapists, and administrative
personnel take over what used to be done by nurses, it becomes increasingly hard to define a function that is uniquely
theirs.

The patient, of course, is not necessarily insulated from

the fallout of this infighting: "Unfortunately, the patient is often the battleground of professional competition; his body, mind, and purse are scarred by the zealous attempts to do for him what each staff member's specialty dictates." [24] And as willing collaboration among categories of functionaries becomes difficult, bureaucratization inevitably takes hold: "As trust becomes more unstable, efforts are made to formulate more and more rules to govern behavior, but the proliferation of rules and the difficulty of writing them in a way that will achieve the desired ends result in inefficiencies and tendencies toward manipulation." [25] The bureaucracy then creates a new occupational niche advertised as filling the void left by the focus of all other occupational categories on their technological expertise; the medical social worker, that is, is said to be an important addition to the hospital work force because "no one else in the hospital has the time and few have the skill to see the patient as a complicated human being in a total environment outside as well as inside the institution." [26]

The physician, whose function could at one time be described as being half of a doctor-patient dyad, "now finds himself the supervisor of a number of paramedical practitioners and only one among several medical specialists. If he is a general practitioner or internist, his role often seems to be that of referee between the various specialists he consults and the paramedical personnel who carry out the care of the patient." [27] And although he and the specialists (or other specialists) all carry the same designation of doctor, it is no longer clear whether they regard themselves as members of a single colleagueship: "At present there is the real question of whether we are the medical profession or the medical professions. . . . That currently this is not completely clear in the minds of many physicians is attested to by the large numbers of physicians who feel much greater loyalty to their individual specialty or guild organization (such as the American College of Physicians, the American Psychiatric Association, or the American College of Surgeons) than they do to the profession as a whole." [28]

This splintering of self-image as well as of expertise culminates in what one observer has called the collusion of anonymity, in which a "difficult" patient "is often seen by several 'eminent' physicians, each of whom gives his opinion about one aspect or another of the problem, but the final responsible decision is seldom explicitly stated even if it has to be taken. If possible, no decision is taken; things are left in suspense until fateful events intervene and make the decision anonymously, allowing everybody to feel that after all it was not his word that counted." [29] Responsibility for the patient, in other words, is diluted, if not surrendered altogether.

In the teaching hospital, this shrugging off of responsibility need not even cross the boundaries of a given specialty; responsibility may simply fall from the shoulders of the patient's "personal" physician to those of the hospital's interns and residents: "No single physician was the patient's only doctor in the hospital even though some high-status patients were made to feel this was so. House staff were always present; they took histories and examined patients. In a crisis they were the first to attend to a hospitalized patient. . . . They exerted considerable influence medically. What they lacked in experience was usually more than made up by the simple fact of their presence." [30] One surgical resident at that same hospital complained: " 'The surgeons in this community enjoy an extraordinary position in that they operate on people day and night and almost never take care of them. . . . Many of these private attendings are not very competent and they leave most of their difficult problems, such as the dying patient, to the house staff.' " [31]

The fragmentation of the doctor side of the doctor-patient dyad becomes a new source of clinical risk. Perhaps the most obvious example is the increased danger of polypharmacy; a study of patients hospitalized because they were suffering from adverse effects of drugs noted the problem that "forty percent of patients receive drugs prescribed by two or more physicians, increasing the possibility of drug interactions." [32] More generally, "The technical aspect of medical care, as a result of specialization, differentiation, and allied phenomena, allows an ever greater possibility for error in the chain of activities (the 'medical assembly line') as the number of individuals involved in the care and treatment of patients increases." [33]

The problem may be more one of competition and disagreement among doctors rather than, or in addition to, a failure of coordination: "Patients with many physicians run the risk of becoming embroiled as innocent victims in disputes over whether surgery or chemotherapy is the appropriate procedure; over the advisable dosage limits to powerful or dangerous drugs; over the jurisdictional boundaries between physicians whose work overlaps. . . . Thus, a patient may find himself rapidly taken off and returned to and again taken off a potentially habit-forming drug; or discover that an intrusive and uncomfortable diagnostic procedure has come to naught because of technical disagreements among physicians on the appropriate methods of analysis." [34]

Confusion, lack of coordination, or outright competition within or between occupations cannot help but risk wounding the patient's psyche as well as his soma. One study of hospitalized patients found "a degree of uncertainty whether physicians and nurses operate as effective teams in close communication. . . . Sometimes patients wonder whether they are sources of conflict and competition between medicine and nursing." [35] Or the patient's being "asked to answer the same questions over and over again leads him to suspect that those who care for him never speak to each other about him and his problems." [36] That an agglomeration of "those who care for him" has replaced a single doctor is itself a source of unease: "From sharing the center of the medical stage with the physician, the patient now often occupies a small corner, outnumbered and overwhelmed by a multitude of white-coated people who speak a cryptic jargon of vaguely reassuring phrases." [37]

Those multitudes may leave the patient feeling like a lump of raw material being processed in a multitude of ways: "No fewer than twenty or thirty different staff persons may well go in and out of his room during the course of the day. Each has a small, sharply defined duty to perform. . . . Patients complain to their visitors that the room is like a railroad station; the continuous coming and going is exhausting and annoying, and, instead of feeling less lonely, they feel psychologically deserted." [38]

What patients are less and less likely to feel is the nurturing, sustaining, ultimately healing effect created by a concern for their well-being communicated by a single doctor in whom they have trust: "Contratherapeutic effects occur not only because the force of orders is spent through a chain of referral, in the sense in which the voltage in a power transmission line drops over distance, but also because the patient as a personality system has strong needs for direct relationship with an identifiable individual helper." [39] When the person he thought of as such a helper calls in, or directs him to, a consultant or physician-collaborator, he may feel confused about his relation to the second doctor and resentful at his apparent abandonment by the first. Or in a teaching hospital he may be dismayed to find that his doctor is no longer his protector, as in the case of the patient who complained: " 'The staff doctor came in and told me, "We do things our way here. Never mind what your doctor said. He doesn't run this hospital. . . ." I felt so helpless. My doctor is really interested in me, and this guy is pushing him around. How can my doctor help me when they don't listen to him?' " [40]

Even if the patient's care is directed by a single physician he can realistically call his, the character of their interaction is likely to be shaped by the fact of that physician's being a modern medical specialist: "The wise man appears not so wise when his knowledge shrinks—even if it coincidentally deepens—to some limited sphere; perhaps more precisely, his wisdom comes to resemble more a technical attribute, less an innate property of his person." [41] The problem for the patient is that his "illness, by its very nature, gives rise to the need for psychological support and pastoral or compassionate care, and the specialist, by the very nature of his 'limited' mandate, even though he has had the standard medical training of all physicians, is simply not ready nor perhaps equipped to provide that kind of care." [42]

In other words, technological expertise on the part of the doctor, however exquisitely refined, may create unease on the part of the patient, even when his somatic pathology is being expertly brought under control. If his somatic pathology eludes technological conquest, or if the process of its conquest itself creates medical complications, unease can easily ripen into anger. And when the technological expertise to which he has been subjected has come from an agglomeration of experts, "the run-around provides the patient with the reasons for blaming one doctor for his impersonal experiences at the hands of many." [43]

5

The Financing of Modern Medical Practice

The physicians, the patients themselves, and the third-party payers all tend not to properly value the synthesizing effort of adapting medical knowledge and procedures to a particular patient. No one pays for it. As a matter of fact, doctors don't charge for it. It is not included in the fee schedule of Blue Shield plans.

RICHARD M. MAGRAW, M.D., *Ferment in Medicine*

In the jargon of the insurance marketplace, you're not even a doctor—you're a "vendor."

GEORGE D. LEMAITRE, M.D., in *Medical Economics*

DOCTORS were entrepreneurs before they were professionals, and when they acquired official recognition as licensed professionals, they managed to retain the benefits of the free market without being subject to its competitive constraints. Doctors were recognized as professionals before they had a science to lay claim to, and when they acquired scientific pretensions, they managed to retain the benefits of their professional and independent-entrepreneurial status, adding on the aura of the scientist without undergoing the self-sacrifice that is part of the folklore of scientific pursuit.

Along the way, doctors in the form of organized medicine have wielded sufficient economic and political power to ensure that the payment mechanisms superimposed on the market for their services—whether private insurance programs or governmental entitlements—have almost universally conformed their workings to the medical fetish of one service, one fee. The cash flow into the doctors' bank accounts, however convoluted in terms of source of funds and route of payment, has simultaneously been increasing in amount and increasingly rewarding what is most product-like about an intimate human service, what is quantifiable, easily labeled, and technologically based—"medical acts" [1] rather than healing relationships.

Payment mechanisms of fee-for-service and insurance based on fee-for-service, together with the structure of medical practice to which they have been added, have brought two kinds of internal conflict to the doctor-patient encounter: there is the more obvious conflict between what is the best treatment for the patient's condition (implying altruism on the doctor's part) and what treatment is most remunerative for the physician, and there is the more subtle conflict between what is best for a sick human being, with a psyche and a social milieu as well as a disordered soma (implying humanistic concern on the doctor's part), and what is most congruent with the scientific model of doctoring as the conquest of somatic pathology. Both conflicts are reinforced by the American secular religion, in whose pantheon both money and science are enthroned as gods. In each situation the payment mechanism serves simultaneously as incentive for a particular action (albeit, only one of many), as shaper of a particular conceptualization of illness and its treatment (again, one of many), and as symbol of what is valued. In general, fee-for-service tends to be linked to the cruder conflict of interest, insurance reimbursement mechanisms to the more subtle one.

The overall level of the income of physicians, as it reflects the high status of medicine generally in American life, further reflects and creates a high valuation of what is most narrow, most activist, and most technologized about American medical practice. Physicians as a whole brought home a mean net income of $51,224 in 1974,[2] which was over four times the median annual earning of American males generically. (The comparison is between physicians and males because the Census Bureau segregates its earnings data by sex; since about 92 percent of American physicians are male, the comparison is in any case reasonably accurate.[3]) Those activist technologists, the surgeons, collected a mean net income of $60,031, while at the other end of the spectrum those who treat by listening and talking, the psychiatrists, earned the relatively low mean net income of $39,997. Obstetrician-gynecologists scored at the high end of the scale ($58,238), while general practitioners and pediatricians did barely better than psychiatrists ($43,808 and $43,429, respectively).[4] As explained by an internist writing in a news magazine, "Somehow or other, a system of physician compensation has developed in this country so that the less a doctor talks to you and the more he does to you the more he is paid." [5]

The way doctors have been paid (whether by patient, private insurer, or public treasury) has been and is predominantly by that pricing mechanism that buys units of treatment, the fee-for-service system. (The other theoretical possibilities are capitation payments, a set amount per patient per year, by which what is bought is responsibility for treatment of a given population; or a salary, by which what is bought is the physician's time. Fee-for-service is usually, although not invariably, associated with the physician working as solo practitioner, while the other financial arrangements are in this country almost always associated with physicians working in groups.)

The fee-for-service system gives the doctor the greatest possible autonomy and the greatest possible ability to augment his income as a direct result of his own efforts, by producing larger numbers of units of treatment and/or higher-priced units of treatment. Larger numbers of units mean shorter encounters, and as one "prominent physician" is quoted as saying, "Time is money to the physician—the less time per professional service, he calculates, means more income to him." [6] More accurately, units of billable service are money, and time is increasingly valuable as it is divided into increasing numbers of units. Talking through the patient's problems, exploring the possible connection between his somatic pain and the sense in which his life is a pain, becomes intolerably unproductive; if a psychiatrist charges $50 for a fifty-minute session, the internist around the corner is probably charging $25 to deal with frequently comparable problems at ten to fifteen minutes per. In such a situation, the prescription pad becomes an increasingly valuable instrument of treatment, for a prescription gives the patient the illusion that he has received something of value for his money, while it takes the doctor only a minute to execute.

But it is in the field of surgery that the fee-for-service system realizes its fullest potential, where it maximally rewards the doctor as activist-faddist. As explained by one insurance expert: "The fee-for-service system, for whatever advantages it may have, has the disadvantage of placing economic incentives on the side of performing more operations [and] more radical operations." [7] While the surgeon is presumed by his mandate as a professional to base his recommendations and actions on the best interests of the patient, fee-for-service rewards him with a fee of perhaps several hundred dollars for operating and of perhaps twenty-five or thirty dollars for giving his expert opinion that surgery is not advisable. This payment system also places a premium on what is new and relatively untested; just as the couture designer commands premium prices for his newest creations, so the superspecialized surgeon commands a premium fee for executing the latest fashion in surgical techniques.

Solo fee-for-service practice is not, however, the only possible route to brief, depersonalized, technologized units of medical treatment. In prepaid group-practice settings, where the prepayment removes the fee barrier to an individual doctor visit, the solvency of the group operation is maintained by not expanding physician supply to meet expanded patient demand. As a result, such settings are typically faced with what their doctors call the overload problem, which they cope with by rushing patients through, frequently ordering batteries of lab tests and X rays to avoid taking the time to perform a thorough history and physical, or shipping the patient off to one of the group's specialists without attempting a careful assessment of the nature of his problem.[8] Surgery is appreciably less frequent in such settings (more surgery creating a greater drain on the organization's prepaid budget),[9] but the surgeons are equally as rushed, aloof, and perfunctory as their colleagues in fee-for-service practice. In both cases financial incentive structures, by opposite routes, reinforce the disvaluation of nurturent care and the valuation of what is quantifiable and presumably scientific.

That value structure finds further reinforcement in the prevailing scheme of private health insurance, a form of casualty insurance providing payment after the fact for items of treatment that fall within the scope of coverage of the insurance policy. Whether from failure of imagination, fear of open-ended costs, or, more likely, the power of the dominant medical mind-set, those policies never promise payment for reassurance, discussion, an expert opinion, or anything else that cannot be defined as a "procedure."

The stereotypical little old lady who worried about her creaky joints and who had some cash in the cookie jar could maneuver the out-of-pocket fee-for-service system so as to obtain frequent administrations of authoritative-sounding encouragement, without either she or her doctor feeling the need for a precise diagnostic label or a technological remedy. Introduce a health insurance policy into the tableau, however, and there follows the need for the doctor's work to fit into the narrow focus of its classificatory scheme. The insurer as source of payment, unlike the cookie jar, has an inherent concern that its funds be spent for particular events that it has made a conscious decision to insure; thus, both thinking in categories and maintaining a system of surveillance of the doctor-patient encounter necessarily accompany insurance, and the terms of insurance begin to influence the terms in which medical treatment is viewed and delivered generally.

Those terms reflect the fact that insurance "involves care of disease and not patient care. Usually the payoff is at the level of disease diagnosis. *It is not the patient but the procedure or disease which is covered.*" [10] So the insurer's transformation of treatment into claim carries with it the risk of "a false standardization of patients' needs and of patients' social situations," in which payment mechanisms "apply to human beings systems of cost control appropriate for securing the most economical production of battery hens." [11] (Oddly enough, although Blue Shield came into being as a creature of organized medicine, the particularized scrutiny of medical practice that flows from such insurance programs is far more searching than what exists when physicians are salaried employees of government.[12])

Just as the surveillance of insurance sanctifies diagnoses and procedures, so it rewards manipulativeness and doctor-patient collusion in conduct bordering on fraud. Records become more important than reality: "Often the doctor is distracted by the need to provide sufficient documentation to convince the insurance carrier that he's delivered a certain service." [13] He is further distracted by the problem of how to deal with the "element of Heisenberg-like indeterminacy in the human realities of medical practice which cannot honestly be made to fit into the blanks of the insurance form." [14] Record and reality become more and more disparate; "a record is a *construction,* not a reflection, of work, and its

substance will vary as the purpose of its producer varies." [15]
And our cultural history comes to include plaintive letters
to the editor, such as the following excerpt:

> Recently I received a bill for $115 for fifteen minutes of a
> doctor's time. When I called to complain, the doctor could
> not understand my motives. "You're insured, aren't you?"
> After some discussion, he told me to pay him what I felt
> was right. However, when I said I would send him $50
> along with the insurance forms, he replied that he would
> have to fill out the forms in the original amount, since to
> reduce the fee would result in his "profile" being lowered
> by the insurance company, thus jeopardizing his right to
> charge his customary fee.[16]

The doctor as rigidified technologist thus becomes the doctor as hustler as well, and the ability to manipulate a claims
form becomes as valued as the ability to interpret an
electrocardiogram.

When the enactment of Medicare and Medicaid in 1965
made the federal government a major health insurer, the
opportunity at least theoretically existed for a national re-
thinking of the conception of doctors' work that had been
created by medicine's scientific pretensions and strengthened by the reimbursement mechanisms of private health insurance. That theoretical opportunity became an early
casualty of a conscious administrative and congressional
strategy of preserving the status quo of the structure of
medical practice and simply grafting these new entitlements
onto it. Medicare has not only honored fee-for-service, it has
further rigidified it by rendering superfluous the altruistic
(if patronizing) medical tradition of treating the elderly
poor at a reduction in fee. It has not only left unthreatened
the categorized way of thinking that accompanies insurance
reimbursement, it has given private insurers a vital role in
program administration and has made of retrospective
claims administration a major new industry.[17]

Both Medicare and Medicaid have carried to new extremes the fee-reimbursement system as incentive to multiple short encounters, as evidenced by sporadic exposés of so-called Medicaid mills, which tend to treat victims of the common cold by having them see three specialists and fill two prescriptions at the pharmacy next door, or of doctors who collect six-figure incomes from Medicare by claiming enormous numbers of visits and administrations of injections to nursing-home patients. The fractionalization of treatment has been encouraged even further, as doctors have discovered the financial advantage of instituting separate charges for services, such as routine lab tests, that used to be lumped into their office-visit fee.[18] The rights to medical care these programs were proudly said to have created have more accurately been rights to call on government to pay for an increasingly segmented, bureaucratized commodity rather than rights to enter into and pursue anything resembling a healing relationship.

Medicare and Medicaid have also enhanced and furthered the delivery of medical treatment as advanced technology, as their generous, cost-based reimbursement formulas for hospital care have paid for whatever expensive new gadgets a hospital's medical staff would like to have at its disposal and have freed their use from the encumbrance of questions about their cost-effectiveness. (Assets per hospital bed, which had risen in value by 18 percent between 1960 and 1965, shot up 54 percent between 1968 and 1973.[19]) What could have been a new way of paying for, structuring, and thinking about medical care became instead an elaboration, almost a caricature, of the old.

When the auto mechanic fails to fix the car, resistance to paying the bill is a natural, universally respected reaction. When the doctor in some sense fails to cure the disease or patch up the injury, the patient's willing acquiescence in his fee nonetheless being paid must depend on there being some difference from the situation of the auto mechanic. That difference might be that the doctor has somehow made clear that he regards a broken arm as a qualitatively different problem from a broken crankshaft, that the patient is to him something other (and more) than a defective machine. Or it might be that, however comfortable his circumstances, material incentives do not appear to be the doctor's primary motivation for pursuing a medical career. One survey of patient attitudes, for example, found that high fees alone were not necessarily problematic: " 'I don't begrudge our doctor a penny of his fees,' " an "Ohio woman" is quoted as saying, " 'as long as he practices good medicine and puts financial considerations last instead of first. He charges a bit more than other doctors, but he doesn't make a big thing about money.' " [20]

Those doctors who do "make a big thing about money" are most likely to find themselves the target of at least the degree of resentment that our hypothetical auto mechanic would inspire. A study of three groups of doctors, one group comprising doctors who had been sued for malpractice two or more times, a second group who had been sued once, and a control group who had never been sued, found that 52 percent of the never-sued doctors said they felt uncomfortable about billing their patients, but only 25 percent of the multiple-suit doctors had that feeling.[21]

But the level of doctors' comfort—and patients' discomfort—with medical-practice-as-business is apparently on the rise: *Medical Economics* sponsored surveys of patient attitudes about doctors in 1969 and 1976, in both cases asking whether the respondent believed the average doctor was "dedicated to helping people more than anything else" or "sees medicine chiefly as a business." In 1969 only 14 percent picked the doctor-as-businessman; in 1976, 48 percent made that choice.[22] The percentage of respondents who thought their doctor's income was excessive rose from 9 percent in 1969 to 24 percent in 1976.[23]

The situation of fee-for-service surgery, as it represents the fullest flowering of that payment mechanism, at the same time represents the optimal breeding ground for patient resentment triggered by money. Of all doctors' fees, the surgeon's fee is most likely to create a hardship for the patient (and doctors have managed not to be bound by the limitations of insurers' fee schedules); of all forms of treatment, an imperfect result of surgical treatment is most likely to make its imperfection painfully obvious; of all doctor-patient combinations, the surgeon and patient are least likely to have had a pre-existing relationship of long standing; and of all doctors, the surgeon is most likely to project a view of his patients as broken-down machinery and of his practice as a well-oiled money machine.

The surgeon in prepaid group practice may, thanks to common training and cultural environment, have a view of his patients and their pathology that is generally comparable to that of the fee-for-service surgeon. But it is the latter— with one nurse checking Blue Shield cards while another fills out forms and sends out bills—who demonstrates how the financing of medical practice can take the view of sick person as defective machine one step further, to a view of medical treatment as commodity to be bought and sold, much like any other product for which the ostensible need is as much created by the manufacturer as it is spontaneously felt by the consumer.

6

The Ideology of Modern Medical Practice

The doctor said that so-and-so indicated that there was so-and-so inside the patient, but if the investigation of so-and-so did not confirm this, then he must assume that and that. If he assumed that and that, then . . . and so on. To Ivan Ilych only one question was important: was his case serious or not? But the doctor ignored that inappropriate question. . . . It was not a question of Ivan Ilych's life or death, but one between a floating kidney and appendicitis.

LEO TOLSTOY, "The Death of Ivan Ilych"

I remember how efficient I was as a house officer in a London hospital; how competent at slipping in the needle; how wondrous at coming up with the right diagnosis. But I also remember, and very bitterly, a general practitioner dying of kidney disease, crying out at midnight for me to hold his hand and comfort him, and my backing away because this I was not able to do nor trained for.

ALAN SHELDON, M.D., "The Efficient Humanist"

THE ideology of modern medical practice has very little to do with the human experience of being sick. It has much more to do with the need of physicians for a conceptual framework that will focus and simplify their work and that will justify the segmented, episodic, superspecialized, individualistic character of their work arrangements. It has something to do with justifying as well an enormous societal investment in medical real estate, high-technology hardware, and drugs. It also has something to do with science, but its increasingly apparent scientific weaknesses make clear that its most important purposes have become other

[78]

than scientific ones, that theory as enlightenment has become ideology as mask.

The theoretical core of modern medical ideology is the germ theory of disease: the notion that particular microscopic agents are the sole cause of particular illnesses. That theory incorporates the disease theory of sickness: the notion that the human experience of being unwell can be adequately explained by a discrete, isolated entity with a reality independent of its manifestation in a particular person. The germ theory of disease has found a generalized form in the doctrine of specific etiology, or causation: the notion that a given disease can be explained by a distinct, well-defined biochemical or physiological abnormality. The whole theoretical, and finally ideological, superstructure is commonly known as the biomedical model: the general assumption that disease reflects disordered biological mechanisms that can ultimately be described in terms of chemistry and physics and that are independent of social behavior or intrapsychic processes. The model is reductionistic, explaining complex phenomena by invoking a single ultimate principle; dualistic, reflecting a separation of mind and body; and mechanistic, reflecting a view of the human body as a machine.[1]

Having been reared by mothers who frequently acted as if germs were the prime enemy of health and well-being, we may find it difficult to imagine a conception of illness that does not grant them a decisive role. In fact, the germ theory and its historic predecessors, which have viewed disease as an attack from outside by an isolated agent—whether a microbe or an evil spirit—have long competed for acceptance with a conception of illness as an ecological disequilibrium within the individual or between the individual and the environment—whether caused by an imbalance of humors, as in the Hippocratic theory, or by impure air and water, as in the view of the nineteenth-century sanitarians. The triumph of the germ theory in the 1870's reflected both the explanatory power of the experimental discoveries made by Pasteur and Koch and the congruence of the theoretical structure they offered with the social and economic environment.

The technological prerequisites of the biomedical model were the autopsy, originally developed for the education of artists in anatomy, and the microscope, originally developed for the observations of naturalists. The autopsy became a reflection and ratification of the mind-body split, for the decision of the Church during the Renaissance to permit human dissection reflected the view that the body was but a temporary vessel for the soul and the understanding that the anatomists would not encroach on the Church's jurisdiction over the soul. "With mind-body dualism firmly established under the imprimatur of the Church, classical science readily fostered the notion of the body as a machine, of disease as the consequence of breakdown of the machine, and of the doctor's task as repair of the machine." [2] The use of the microscope to study microorganisms, begun by van Leeuwenhoek in the seventeenth century, led to the study of cell structure and the development in the mid-nineteenth century of cellular pathology, the view of disease as altered structure. It thus made possible (though not inevitable) a way of thinking about disease that not only excluded mind but also excluded environment, social and physical—an individualistic biology divorced from population biology.

Pasteur's enunciation of the germ theory coincided with Darwin's enunciation of the theory of evolution. [3] As a form of Darwinism became a rationalization of competitive individualism in the economic sphere, so it also shaped the developing contours of the germ theory. When Pasteur in France and Koch in Germany produced disease by injecting virulent microorganisms into healthy laboratory animals, it was easy to view these results in light of the Darwinian concept of a struggle of living things for survival and then to focus on defeating the microbe rather than on altering the environment so as to strengthen the resistance of the host. Such an aggressive view of how to approach disease was also congruent with the prevailing conception of human progress as an ever-increasing mechanical domination over nature.

There were competing views of disease and its proper treatment. Pidoux in France, an avid opponent of Pasteur's theories, advocated the concept of diathesis, explaining disease as "the common result of a variety of diverse external and internal causes . . . bringing about the destruction of an organ by a number of roads which the hygienist and the physician must endeavor to close." [4] Virchow in Germany (who in 1855 developed cellular pathology) served in 1847 on a commission to study a typhus epidemic in the industrial districts of Upper Silesia and wrote a minority report arguing that the epidemic had been triggered by a famine resulting from crop failure due to heavy rains, combined with a severe winter that had forced the poor, cold and hungry, to huddle together.[5] He subsequently wrote: "Medicine is a social science, and politics nothing but medicine on a grand scale." [6] In France and Germany, the opponents of the germ theory had little effect; in England and America, they initiated sanitary reforms and founded the study of public health, but it remained separate from, and posed no threat to, the development of clinical medicine as a scientific discipline based on the germ theory.[7]

For the medical practitioners the germ theory was much more serviceable than an environmental approach to the treatment of illness, for it justified their one-to-one relationships with members of the upper classes, whose living and working environments were in any event less unhealthy than those of the poor.[8] The germ theory, together with its more generalized successor, the doctrine of specific etiology, implied that controlling disease requires specific interventions, chemical or physical, instituted by individual physicians. The impressive results emerging from the research labora-

tories, combined with the interests of the prestigious physicians who dominated the teaching hospitals and medical
education generally, combined to enthrone the biomedical
model as the conventional medical wisdom and eventually
(especially after the 1930's, when its technological applica-
tions began to spew forth in accelerating numbers) as folk
wisdom as well. Sickness became disease, and disease became a somatic lesion in the body of the individual; treatment became an after-the-fact attack focused on that lesion,
bypassing both the psyche of the individual whose body was
diseased and his social and physical environment.

None of this is to imply that Pasteur and Koch fabricated
the association of disease with the injection of microbes into
laboratory animals, or to argue that microbes have nothing
to do with illness. It is to imply that such a controlled procedure in such an artificial environment bears no resem-
blance to the process by which a human being gets sick,
that, as Dubos points out, "by the skillful selection of experimental systems, Pasteur, Koch, and their followers succeeded in minimizing in their tests the influence of factors
that might have obscured the activity of the infectious
agents they wanted to study." [9] Such factors would have involved either the internal state of the infected individual or
the state of his external environment.

The biomedical model spawned by the germ theory fails,
for example, to account for the common situation of an individual being host to an assortment of microbes without
becoming sick, because it has excluded from consideration
the internal ecology of the individual and the phenomena of
resistance to infection and ecological balance.[10] By also
excluding from its purview the ecological system of the individual in relation to his external environment, the biomedical model has suffered other failures: "With little understanding of the way of life to which man is biologically
adapted, modern medicine is unable to predict the possible
harmful consequences of departures from it. It was 'sur-

prised' to find that the repeated inhalation of tobacco smoke actually harmed the lungs and caused cancer." [11] And it has been handicapped by its failure to consider the interactions between an individual's physical state and his "psychophysiologic responses to life change"; such interactions may in fact "alter susceptibility and thereby influence the time of onset, the severity, and the course of a disease," [12] meaning, for example, that the likelihood of a metabolic dysfunction assuming the form of diabetes increases if and when the individual loses his job or his spouse.

If the biomedical model does not serve the function of adequately explaining the human experience of sickness, its survival for a century relatively unscathed must mean that it has served other functions that in some sense have been equally significant. Those functions have had to do with rationalizing a particular structure of medical practice and more generally with providing the protective coloration of scientific mystification to vested interests in the medical sphere and beyond.

The inward focus of the biomedical model justifies, even glorifies, an emphasis on curative, rather than preventive, medicine. Given, that is to say, the importance of environmental factors in prevention of illness, medicine's concentration on internal biological phenomena has denigrated the task of prevention and has meant that its curative technology is much more developed than its preventive abilities. This result, in turn, has minimized the possibility that medicine might pose a threat to established interests in the larger society. "To the medical-care system and to the larger political economy, a major usefulness of the technological, market commodity, curative definition of medical care is that it obscures the social origin of so many ills—their roots in the social order—and diverts attention from the social interventions that would constitute real change." [13]

As it reinforced curative medicine, the biomedical model vindicated the individualistic entrepreneurships that medical practitioners had long before established. If illness represents isolated episodes of localized pathology, then it is appropriate for the physician to concern himself only with the immediate problem of the individual patient, rather than with the ongoing problems of a person in a familial and social environment, to set a price for each isolated encounter, and to maintain the freedom to take on or discharge particular patients as he wishes. The biomedical model has been conveniently congruent, in other words, with the class interests of the professionals: "Part and parcel of professional performance and the ideology surrounding it are the historical accretions of an occupational status and the social origins of its incumbent. Being predominantly from the bourgeoisie, the professional emphasizes independence, social and economic individualism, and class dignity in his status." [14]

The biomedical model has adapted well to the fragmentation of the medical profession into specialties. If disease exists at the microbiological level, after all, it is natural to parcel out the organs of the human body among an assortment of specialized clinicians. The model is also reflected in the structure of insurance reimbursement, where it justifies extending coverage for isolated technological procedures rather than for an ongoing doctor-patient dialogue.

The biomedical model has provided the ideological underpinnings of, and has in turn been nourished by, the activities of the biomedical research establishment and the drug industry in their development of modern medicine's enormous armamentarium of medications: "Whatever the nature of the disease, the most important task—so at least is the well-nigh universal belief—is to discover some magic bullet capable of reaching and destroying the responsible demon within the body of the patient." [15] A booklet produced by the Pharmaceutical Manufacturers Association can claim with apparent plausibility that "the growing and diverse contributions of the [pharmaceutical] industry to health care comprise a monumental chapter in man's eternal battle against disease and death." [16]

Medical activism in all situations is stimulated and validated by the biomedical model. Even imminent death becomes "the ultimate challenge to [the physician's] abilities instead of the natural, inevitable, biological phenomenon that it is. All that was necessary to avoid it were better diagnostic tools, bigger, better and more powerful drugs, and the advanced technology to replace or repair those organs whose structural disorder had reached an irreversible stage." [17] The biomedical model makes of doctors the priests of a secular religion, a variant of the more general secular faith that technology is the answer to all worldly ills and that what is newer is by definition better.

If the doctor has become a secularized priest, the hospital has become a secularized shrine, transformed by medical engineering from a site of passive caretaking into an activist treatment center. The enterprise of the medical center, a complex of superspecialized equipment manipulated by an army of superspecialized personnel, has spawned an updated version of the biomedical model, what one academic physician has called "the 'excellence' deception in medicine": "The dominant medical leadership and its establishment are not primarily engaged in the disinterested pursuit of knowledge and translation of that knowledge into medical practice; rather, in significant part they are engaged in special interest advocacy, pursuing and preserving social power. The concept of excellence is a component of the ideological justification of that role." [18]

The ideology of excellence assures us that treatment administered in the hospital (preferably a teaching hospital) is inherently superior to treatment administered in less technological settings. "The best medical care," to quote another academic physician spouting the conventional wisdom, "is achieved in an environment of constant inquiry and scrutiny by a number of people (medical students, house-staff interns and residents, senior-staff professors and practicing physicians), where scientific and technical knowledge can be applied within the shortest period of time after its development. . . . Ideally all hospitals should be affiliated with medical schools." [19] Such bland assertions of the ideology of institutional excellence, as opposed to serious inquiries into the effectiveness of high-technology medical treatment, are the norm of discourse on the subject: "Despite the widespread self-designation of excellence in medicine, few definitions of excellence are found in either the medical literature or the policy statements of medical institutions. Operationally, excellence is simply that which the leaders of the professions and its institutions do." [20] What they do has very little to do with healing the sick and much more to do with manipulating diseased bodies as if they were specimens in a laboratory. "Medical practice is needlessly complicated, redundant, ineffective, and, per procedure conducted, inefficient." [21]

The minute fragmentation of treatment that is a distinguishing characteristic of the modern medical center, along with the competing struggle for status of its proliferating paramedical occupations, is then incorporated into the mythology of excellence via the concept of the health-care team. The task-oriented structure of hospital workers' work (the medical technician taking blood, the X-ray technician taking X rays) is less justified by the technology it involves than it is rationalized by the assumption of the underlying biomedical model that it is appropriate to deal with the patient in terms of pieces of his anatomy, for his status as an integrated human being has nothing to do with his disease. It then becomes possible for the hospital administrator to rationalize his goal of maximizing employee productivity and passivity through the repetition of routinized tasks by calling it teamwork, the hospital bureaucracy wearing the mask of the health-care team.

The biomedical model and the ideology of excellence

thus inevitably downgrade the interpersonal aspects of the encounter between patient and doctor or hospital worker, such considerations being shrugged off as unscientific. "Physicians know little about the behavioral sciences; when they do mention them they tend to deprecate the possible contributions these sciences may make to an understanding of the care of patients." [22] Conversely, what comes to be emphasized is the thingness aspect of treatment; if cure rather than care is the only goal worthy of scientific medicine and if what is being cured is an isolable somatic lesion, then the patient is appropriately seen as a consumer of discrete drugs and procedures rather than as a participant in a continuous social process.

The doctor's view of his patient and his role is then narrowed and focused: "Our finest academic institutions tend to produce physicians who are so completely preoccupied with the complex liturgy of molecular biology, biochemistry and pathophysiology that they tend to look upon the patient as a curious vessel for the containment of interesting pathology." [23] The role of the physician, then, "is to rid the patient of those noxious agents on which we are doing research." [24] That the narrowness of that mind-set can be problematic was observed in an exhaustive study of a prestigious teaching hospital: "The physician focused his interest on physical disease; he was usually not concerned with personal and social influences in relation to the disease. . . . The problems of the patient were viewed in a physiologic or 'mechanistic' context. The stigma of mental illness was avoided, but at a price: Links between disease and what we call a way of life . . . were not considered in diagnosis. This led to underdiagnosing obvious mental disorders and misdiagnosing some physical disorders." [25]

The type of person who enters medical school and the self-perceived role of his teachers then narrows in turn. According to a member of the Harvard Medical School faculty: "If you're the kind of guy who goes to college and gets into lots of extracurricular activities, gets B's, and likes to work with people, you're not getting into medical school any more. . . . The kind of physician people dream about is not getting into medical school any more." [26] According to a physician teaching at Yale: "We are training researchers first, practitioners second. Those who enter practice are usually the second-rate students and some say we should teach them how to practice. But I feel we shouldn't waste our time on them." [27]

And the biomedical model and the role of the researcher continue to be glorified. A leading figure in the biomedical research establishment, for example, argues that "what we need is more science, not less. We should not be talking about abandoning modern medicine; it is not yet really here. When we have it as a genuine science . . . the technology of medicine will be easy to deliver, and will no longer cost the moon." [28] It is clear from the context that "science" does not include, for example, population biology, the physiology of stress, cultural anthropology, or psychoanalysis (the same person has said elsewhere that "psychosomatic medicine is on its way out" [29]). Although broadening the scope of medicine's purview would not inevitably make it less scientific, the defenders of biomedicine would limit that designation to what falls more or less within the purview of microbiology. In the words of a physician-critic of the biomedical model: "Lack of progress in the understanding of the human dimensions of illness and patient care may . . . be traced to the neglect of its scientific study. The anti-intellectual and antiscience cabal we have to combat are not the ignorant in the streets but those in authority who deny the applicability of science to the study of man in health and disease." [30]

The narrow perspective of biomedicine creates for the sick individual an exaggerated dependence on the members of the medical profession. If, that is to say, a person and his doctor discussed his backaches, headaches, or bellyaches in the context of his life situation, they might jointly conclude that, rather than immediately proceed with a battery of diagnostic tests or a long-term regimen of medication, it would be worth the patient's while to attempt a change in his job, his marriage, his neighborhood, his diet, his activities, or his general manner of relating to other people. At the end of such an encounter the patient would have become not a passive, dependent recipient of biomedicine's technological largesse but a self-directed seeker of therapeutic change, although along the way he might seek expert guidance, even from someone with an M.D. degree.

What makes such a scenario almost a fantasy reflects the threats it would pose to the vested interests that are protected by the biomedical model. The physician would lose not only income from return visits but also the psychological gratification of feeling that the patient is dependent on his professional expertise. The pharmaceutical industry would not only lose a customer in the immediate sense but would possibly also lose a participant in the lifelong symbiotic relationship with that industry that most people enter into, much to its profit. The whole referral structure of specialists, diagnostic equipment, and hospitals would suffer a loss of both income and the exalted status it has come to be accorded. In many cases employers, landlords, and others with power over people's life conditions might suffer a challenge to their freedom to make people sick.

By removing the patient and his social setting from the causality system of illness, the biomedical model deprives the patient of the possibility of making himself well. If, that is to say, being sick means being a passive, innocent victim of an invasion of microbes or some other alien elements, then getting well logically involves passively permitting an expertly trained mercenary to wage battle with them. This is not to advocate the contrary extreme, to suggest, for example, that a child suffering from lead poisoning should be saddled with responsibility for the lead paint on the walls

of his family's apartment. It is rather to argue that in excluding psychological, social, and environmental factors
from its purview, the biomedical model precludes the possibility of individuals seeking health at least in part by changing their life situation and challenging their life conditions.
Nor is it to suggest that the jet-setter whose ski injuries seem
to reflect self-destructive inclinations should have his broken
bones left unset, simply that they represent only a portion of
his sickness.

In the end, the biomedical model calls into question even
the validity of the patient's subjective experience of being
sick: "A feature of the 'modern' medical system . . . is
that one can feel well and be told he has a disease, feel sick
and be told he has no disease, and last, show a state of social maladaptation and be told he is deviant, but neither
sick nor diseased." [31] The patient's life experience becomes
irrelevant to the modus operandi of the doctor, which in
turn becomes increasingly incomprehensible to the patient
as it retreats further into a realm that doctors call science
and patients perceive as magic.[32] As one hospital study
found, "sometimes . . . 'scientific' medicine was used as
'insulating' medicine between patients and physicians. In
that process the physician assumed superior knowledge and
discounted or even ignored the report of the patient." [33] The
biomedical model, in other words, insults the patient's sense
of selfhood by denying the reality of his experience.

The meanings doctors and patients give to illness become
ever more divergent. "Differences in orientation mean that
a false consensus prevails between the doctor and the patient. This type of consensus can lead to the use of a set of
key terms in the relationship, but they actually mean very
different things to each person." [34] When the patient comes
to realize that the doctor is not responding to what he con-
siders the reality of his problem, the result is frustration on
his part countered by resentment on the doctor's part. "The
frustration of those who find what they believe to be their

legitimate health needs inadequately met by too technologically oriented physicians is generally misinterpreted by the biomedical establishment as indicating 'unrealistic expectations' on the part of the public rather than being recognized as reflecting a genuine discrepancy between illness as actually experienced by the patient and as it is conceptualized in the biomedical mode." [35]

Biomedicine, in sum, creates in laypeople an exaggerated dependency on doctors but at the same time fails to satisfy the needs and expectations that lead people to obediently fall into the passive receptivity of the patient role. Medical practitioners and organizations then express surprise and outrage that people are ungrateful for the marvels scientific medicine has brought them and that instead of passively resigning themselves to the risk these marvels invariably entail, they are increasingly suing their doctors when risk becomes injury.

7

The Commodification of Healing

*"He makes me feel like something on a production line," com-
plains a middle-aged woman in Indiana. "If I speak up—
about his fee or anything else—he glares at me, as much as
to say, 'How dare you try to be a human being!' "*

An article in *Medical Economics*,
reporting on its 1976 Patient Attitude Survey

*In manufacturing we do not concern ourselves with the tor-
tures through which fibers, plastics, metals or the like are put
in the course of the production process. But in the human services we are concerned that the course of providing help include some sensitive recognition of and responsiveness to the
human quality of the structure of flesh and bone being processed. Responsiveness and recognition themselves may constitute the service and its benefit; without it, the encounter is
dead and the service provided to a mere object, albeit not one
of fiber, plastic or metal.*

ELIOT FREIDSON, *Doctoring Together*

THE developing character of modern medical practice
has made the doctor-patient dyad less and less a healing
relationship and more and more a market transaction; thus,
the commodification of healing. The process involves both
discrete exchanges replacing ongoing associations and technocrats engaged in commerce replacing healers engaged
in a calling, both thingness replacing human relatedness
and economics replacing ethics. Aspects of commodification attach to the patient, to what happens to the patient in
the name of medical treatment, and even to the doctor.

The change in the character of medical treatment that
the rubric commodification encompasses has been a process
not of the medical profession imposing something on the

larger society but of something gradually emerging from the mutual interactions between medicine and the social forces at work in the larger society. And while it represents a historical process, commodification has a mythical aspect as well: our sense of deprivation in the present, that is to say, leads us to glorify our perception of the past, and the contrast we feel becomes as much a contrast between what is and what we think should be as between what is and what really was.

"Relationship" implies continuity, a sense of ongoing obligation, and an interaction that penetrates the human façade. It fits the situation of the doctor making a house call, responding to the latest crisis of sickness in a family (the family, not an individual member of it, being in reality the patient), entering as an honored guest into the family's own environment, taking what he sees in that environment into account as he questions and advises, and sharing his opinions and concern with everyone there. "Transaction" implies a discrete encounter for a limited purpose, the parties relating in a way that is superficial, impersonal, distanced. It fits the situation of the patient coming into the doctor's examining room, split off from his natural surroundings, discarding the social amenities that in such a setting are out of place, the doctor being limited by his specialty to treating at most one generation of the family, if not one isolated member.

"Healing," as the character of a relationship, implies trust flowing from the sick person to the healer, altruistic concern flowing from the healer to the sick person. Trust need not inevitably involve mystification or awe, just as altruistic concern need not inevitably involve authoritarian paternalism. Both together set in motion a process in which the sick person, viewing the healer with an attitude of expectant faith,[1] grants the healer the opportunity to mobilize and bolster the recuperative powers inherent in the sick person himself, the healer giving the sick person empathy and thereby strength, and drawing off the anxieties, doubts, and fears that inhibit self-healing. (The process has elements of the non-rational, in the sense that it draws on unconscious forces; on the other hand, it is not irrational, meaning against reason, when it does not contradict the sick person's best interest but operates to further it.)

"Market," as the character of a transaction, implies that something, a product or a service, is being sold for a profit; it describes a situation subtly different from one in which assistance is furnished by someone who in some manner is paid for his work but in which a monetary exchange is not seen as a central feature of what is going on. The market aspect appears most clearly when the patient emerges from a visit to the doctor feeling that he has bought a prescription or an operation (perhaps being asked to pay the fee before he even leaves the premises); in such a case the kinship is obvious between the pitch for Geritol on the television screen and the pitch for coronary artery bypass surgery in the consulting room. In the words of one economic analyst: "We have a national consensus for good health. One problem is that somehow we have been educated to think we can buy it." [2]

Just as a commercial for a car or a detergent is selling both a product and the lure of success and happiness, or just as a hairdresser is selling both a service and an aura of beauty, so the modern doctor is selling both medical treatment and the expectation of that amorphous quality we call health. He and his patient have both brought to their encounter the unspoken assumption that living is consuming; after all, "a substantial minority of physicians lean heavily on paid advertisements by drug corporations in their professional journals for news of innovations, while the primary source of health information among their patients is advertisement on commercial television." [3] Health becomes a thing rather than a way of living, and the doctor becomes a purveyor (and the patient a consumer) of things—pills and procedures—rather than a participant in a way of relating. In the process it is not surprising that the patient himself becomes a thing—an objectified lesion as seen on an X-ray film, an electrocardiogram, or a computer printout from the lab, a defective machine to be repaired (with the products and processes of modern technology), rather than a sick human being whose inherent healing powers need to be encouraged and reinforced.

Language then comes both to reflect evolving perceptions of what medical treatment means and to accelerate the process of changing perceptions. "Industrial terminology has become increasingly common in the language of the health professions. Not long ago, the medical profession became a sector of the health care *industry*. Nurses, occupational therapists, and physicians were transformed into health *workers*. They became *providers* and the patients became *consumers*. . . . The use of rather cold, distant labels such as 'consumer' and 'provider' removes the sense of personal involvement between patient and doctor, and may contribute to less satisfied, less trusting 'consumers' and 'providers' alike." [4]

The physician's practice, meanwhile, with some prodding from physicians' management journals and professional management firms, assumes the characteristics of the high-priced consultantships that have proliferated in the world of commerce. He increasingly keeps a five-day (or four-and-a-half-day) week, hiding at other times behind his answering service; he increasingly charges standardized prices, being spared by insurance, private and public, from any sense of obligation to consider the individual circumstances of his clientele; he increasingly transforms himself, with or without associates, into a professional corporation, gaining the tax-free fringe benefits and tax-deferred retirement plan that go with the status of corporate executive; and he increasingly asks his customers to pay up at the time of their visit to his office.[5] He learns to augment his produc-

tivity (after he learns to think in terms of productivity) by
hiring more paraprofessionals and adding more examining
rooms. He becomes "the true executive, protected from the
public by an army of nurses, secretaries, receptionists, and
answering services." [6] In turn, he comes to be perceived less
as a dedicated humanitarian and more as a shrewd, unfeel-
ing businessman: "The 'Doctor,' the public and the press
began to say, is a man who . . . drives a Cadillac or a
Continental, orders the largest steak at a restaurant, is rude
and arrogant with patients, and has two home phone numbers, two office numbers, and a 24-hour answering service,
but can never be reached." [7]

As doctor and patient become more distanced and their
interactions become more segmented, the doctor himself becomes more commodified, a set of credentials rather than a
special kind of person. "The patient can count on neither
his commonality with the physician in the local community
nor on the fraternity of local physicians as grounds for
trust. Authority is increasingly technical in its base; the
doctor as replaceable technician, to be judged like any
other, is a plausible definition." [8] Universal science replaces
individual talent: "Increasingly, the glory of the doctor as a
person fades, while his scientific practices glow with promise. Far from being seen as completely unique individuals,
doctors are coming to be regarded as interchangeable because they all have approximately the same training." [9]

As people increasingly view doctors as embodiments of
objectified credentials, they increasingly view themselves as
consumers of something called health services, not as patients taking part, with a doctor and possibly others, in an
interactive process called healing. Ultimately, the participants on both sides of the medical encounter see themselves,
each other, and what transpires between them as disem-
bodied, objectified, commodified abstractions in a setting
stripped down to its economic and technological com-
ponents.

The commodification process is fed by all the various trends in, and aspects of, modern medical practice that we have been considering. Its way is eased by medical technology: drugs and operations are easily seen as cognates of commercial products and services; lab tests and other forms of diagnostic technology make it easy for the doctor virtually to ignore the patient and focus on detached, objectified evidence of pathology; hospitals increasingly take on the appearance of sterilized factories for reconditioning half-used bodies. Technology, however, does not itself make commodification inevitable—witness the liberating and humanizing effect a motorized wheelchair can have on a quadriplegic or the therapeutic value of the telephone to someone who is bedridden. In both cases technology enhances the individual's ability to be active and self-directed —attributes of health—in contrast, for example, to the technological accouterments of an intensive-care unit, which force a patient into maximum passivity.

In the final analysis, however, the question is less whether medical treatment draws on technological innovation than whether the patient whose treatment *does* draw on technological innovation is recognized as an end in himself or is used primarily as a means to some other end, whether income or a boosted ego to the doctor; profit or legitimacy to the pharmaceutical or medical-supply industry; solvency or institutional maintenance to the hospital; or prestige, intellectual games playing, or the training of new generations of medical technocrats to the biomedical research and teaching establishment. It is not necessarily problematic for drugs or surgery to be used to effect a cure that would otherwise be impossible, but it is problematic for doctors and hospitals to function primarily as eager consumers of high-technology, quickly obsolescent medical products, patients becoming mere adjuncts of the chemicals and hardware and being lured themselves into medical-product addiction and their own dehumanization.

In alliance with the worship of technology, the splintering of the medical profession exacerbates commodification. What used to distinguish the doctor as general practitioner from the merchant was his acceptance of an ongoing responsibility to provide broadly defined services to his clientele. But specialization enables the doctor to decline to take on what he can plausibly characterize as falling within the particularized expertise of another specialty, with the result that his patients find themselves strung out among a collection of practitioners, their connection to any one of whom is too tenuous to offer much sustenance.

Putting the patient in the hospital, as is more and more commonly the practice, carries the splintering process and the concomitant shrugging off of medical responsibility still further. Here there may be interns and residents as well as assorted full-fledged specialists, and there will in any event be an array of technicians and various grades of nurses. Commodification in this setting transforms the patient into an object on a minutely divided assembly line, worked over by a swarm of personnel who typically spend less than a minute each carrying out their various narrowly focused tasks. Commodification is then strengthened by the increasing standardization of the length of the hospital stay, effected in the name of cost and quality control, the patient becoming a diagnosis-and-age combination to be treated and discharged according to a predetermined statistical formula.

Commodification as standardization is encouraged further by insurance financing, which tends to reduce patients to Blue Cross numbers and patient care to identifiable procedures entered in boxes on a claims form. A bureaucratic pall descends over the process of obtaining treatment, and getting admitted to the hospital becomes much like establishing credit with the electric company. (As a so-called patient representative told Studs Terkel: "People see hospitals as money first and health second. On our admitting forms we ask all these questions—next of kin, who's gonna pay the bill?—and fill out all these blank squares. The *last* question is: 'What is wrong with you, sir?' " [10])

Commodification is crowned by the biomedical model: "Knowledge is considered to be a commodity to be secured by a few and sold to the many. Schools and professional institutions are structured to facilitate that relationship." [11] The patient becomes consumer of esoteric mumbo-jumbo, and the content of that mumbo-jumbo denies his holistic humanness and commodifies his sickness by defining it as a discrete somatic lesion and its treatment as a battle plan for technological obliteration.

The upshot is that being cured of one's recognized disease is frequently accompanied by being wounded in other parts of one's personhood, a state that risks compromising the effectiveness of the cure narrowly defined. The upshot is also an attitude toward doctors that is ambivalent at best: "On the one hand, admiration is directed at the scientific and technological achievements of medicine and its 'miracles'; on the other, there is a fair amount of hostility toward the medical profession in terms of the kinds of incomes and other rewards they are able to garner and display, their apparent decreasing interest in their individual patients, their unwillingness to make house calls, their brusque behavior, crowded waiting rooms, and so on." [12]

But the commodification of healing logically means "the increasing application of the laws of the marketplace—of legalized and legitimated doctor-patient hostility." [13] If patients see medical treatment being sold like the goods and services they buy in the commercial arena—if hiring a surgeon to rearrange one's interior anatomy becomes comparable to hiring a contractor to remodel one's basement—then it is only natural that patients feel anger and seek economic redress when the medical product or service turns out to be in some sense defective. That anger might even be greater than what being wronged in the commercial sphere would evoke, for the available remedies are fewer: "Medical care cannot be returned to the seller for a money-back refund; it cannot be taken back for repairs if it goes wrong; nor can one cut one's losses and throw it away." [14] Such a comparison would be ludicrous if medical treatment were seen as a special sort of relationship—characterized by, among other qualities, an inevitable element of uncertainty as to its outcome. The comparison becomes plausible when patients begin to sense that they are being treated like customers,[15] like ciphers in the sphere of economics rather than human beings in the sphere of ethics.

II

The Malpractice Crisis

8

The Malpractice Crisis as Distortion

At this stage it's debatable whether medical malpractice is even an insurable risk; maybe it should be considered like floods or earthquakes. An "industry observer" quoted in *The Wall Street Journal*, January 30, 1975

WHEN an unhappy patient decides to sue his doctor for malpractice, that decision has something to do with medical treatment. When an unhappy insurance company decides to get out of the business of insuring doctors against their patients suing them for malpractice, that decision has virtually nothing to do with medical treatment. Mostly it has to do with such esoteric insurance-economic concepts as long tails, narrow bases, and drains on surplus.

But the unhappy patient—or even thousands of unhappy patients—at most has a problem; he lacks the power to transform that problem into a crisis—a problem generally perceived as endangering the social fabric and thus demanding an immediate social response. The unhappy insurance company does have that power, or at least has the economic power to jerk the loose thread that threatens to unravel the social fabric. But because the underlying problem is, after all, the problem of the patient, not of the insurance company, the crisis becomes a distortion of the underlying problem.

One of the more striking characteristics of the malpractice crisis of the 1970's, in short, is that unhappy patients were unable to bring it about. Although real increases in the

[103]

number of malpractice claims being filed and the amount of damages being sought had been occurring since the middle to late 1960's, and although those increases had received sporadic official attention in the late sixties and early seventies,[1] the malpractice problem only achieved the status of a full-blown crisis in the public eye when the rise in claims was combined with external economic circumstances that threatened the profitability of the insurance industry. It thus becomes necessary to navigate at least some of the intricacies of insurance economics in order to understand what created the disjunction between the public debate about the malpractice crisis and the ultimate sources of the malpractice problem—to avoid mistaking appearance for reality.

The fact that doctors and hospitals were able to buy insurance protection against the risk of being held legally liable for a patient's injuries and the fact that they came to buy such insurance protection routinely had given to the private, profit-making entities comprising the insurance industry a dominant role in the system of allocating losses due to medical negligence. Questions of medical injury (or of the anger of patients who felt themselves victimized by medical practice) had then become subsumed to questions of the profitability of the loss-allocation system under insurance principles of spreading the risk.

What then transformed the malpractice problem into a crisis was the decision of much of the insurance industry that the attempt to apply those insurance principles to the legal liability of doctors and hospitals had become inherently unprofitable. In late 1974 and early 1975 that decision was translated into a string of announcements by several carriers in strategic locations that they were raising malpractice insurance premiums to unthinkable levels or that they were walking away from the business altogether. Within a few months what had been a chronic, sporadically noticed problem for almost a decade suddenly became a crisis demanding the urgent attention of all sources of influence and power in the society.

Insurance principles begin with the fact that the insurance product is a promise to take financial responsibility for defined losses under defined circumstances and during a defined period of time—losses that may or may not occur. In buying the product, the customer (the insured) transfers a potential cost from himself to his insurance carrier. The carrier, in turn, is in business to operate a cost-transfer system, in which it collects premiums from large numbers of insureds and pays the losses of a few. In the case of liability insurance, the insurer's promise to pay is supplemented by a promise to perform a service, namely, to investigate and defend all claims made charging the insured with legal liability to some third party.[2]

An insurer can make (or lose) money in two ways. The most obvious is from its underwriting operations, in which it makes money by taking in more in premiums than it pays out in losses combined with costs of operation (known in the trade as an underwriting profit). The less obvious but for our purposes equally important profit-producing (or loss-producing) mechanism is the investment of the sizable amounts of money represented by premiums. A given year's operation, that is to say, may produce an underwriting loss but an overall profit thanks to compensating income from investment; an insurer may even be willing to take a large risk of underwriting losses on a particular line of insurance precisely because that line for some reason offers the prospect of generous investment income.[3]

Medical professional liability insurance, as medical malpractice insurance is formally known, is a subset of professional liability insurance, which in turn is a subset of what is usually called the property/liability insurance industry, as distinguished from the life and health insurance industry. One feature that has distinguished the property/liability arm of the insurance industry is that property/liability carriers, especially since the early 1970's, have been investing increasing proportions of their portfolios in common stocks, rather than preferred stocks or bonds.[4]

From a doctor's point of view, the basic purpose of malpractice insurance is to protect his assets (house, car, boat, bank account) from legalized seizure to satisfy a judgment won by a former patient who has successfully sued him for malpractice. In the not-too-distant past most hospitals were protected from malpractice suits by one or the other of two arcane and archaic legal doctrines, the doctrine of charitable immunity for private, non-profit hospitals and the doctrine of sovereign immunity for public hospitals. By the time the crisis broke, however, legislatures and courts in most states had eliminated such protection as anachronistic, and hospitals too had entered the market for malpractice insurance as asset protection.

From the insurance industry's point of view, medical malpractice insurance has always been a very small line with some very peculiar characteristics, which have made it attractive or repellent, depending mostly on external economic circumstances at the time and partly on the character of the individual carrier making the judgment. As is true of most so-called facts in the medical malpractice morass, the fact of the relative size of this line of insurance is difficult to pin down; estimates of its pre-crisis size in terms of its premium volume as a percentage of premium volume for the entire property/liability insurance industry ranged from 1.1 percent [5] through 2.3 percent [6] to "less than 7" percent.[7] Whichever estimate is the most accurate, the absolute smallness of the market has made actuaries calculating premiums very nervous. And its relative smallness has made insurance managements much inclined to stop underwriting the line altogether when it becomes more than a little troublesome.

The smallness problem is known to insurers as the problem of a narrow base, or of low credibility, meaning that to establish the odds of a risk coming to fruition with any degree of accuracy requires a large universe of exposures to that risk. As explained by one actuary to one of the numerous conferences that have been held to discuss the malpractice crisis:

> Credibility is an actuarial problem dealing with the amount of trust that we put into any rate scheme. My company [Chubb & Son, Inc.] writes [i.e., underwrites] a State group in New Jersey with between 7,000 and 8,000 doctors, and we rate the program as an independent entity. This, as an actuary, makes me a little uneasy. I wouldn't consider making rates for that few automobiles. I would demand several more thousand, maybe a few hundred thousand, in order to be sure of the rates that I was charging, especially if I am going to slice the experience up into the various classifications for pricing.[8]

The slicing alluded to refers to the practice of separating physicians into various categories and establishing a separate premium rate for each. In the relatively distant past all doctors in a given locality paid the same premium for their malpractice insurance, but at some point—varying from circa 1950 to circa 1960, depending on the source [9]—carriers decided to develop a rate structure that would at least partially reflect the fact that an orthopedic surgeon faces a greater risk of being sued than a psychiatrist. The number of rate classifications being used has varied from five to eleven, and classification by specialty grouping is sometimes combined with classification by location within a state; New York, for example, has had seven specialty classifications and four geographical classifications.[10] Whatever the theoretical equity of the procedure in terms of allocating the cost of insurance, for the carriers it has only intensified the problem of actuarial credibility by fragmenting an already narrow base of insureds.

An actuary's nervousness in contemplating the narrow base of a malpractice insurance program is likely to become acute anxiety when he contemplates the long tail that goes with it—although his hot-shot superiors may have decided that the long tail can lead to a pot of gold. When insurance people talk about tails, they are referring to the length of time that elapses between the event that triggers a claim and the final resolution of the claim.

If a homeowner's home burns down, he is likely to file a claim with the insurance company that sold him fire insurance more or less immediately, and a settlement between the two parties is likely to follow without much delay; thus, fire insurance has a short tail. If the homeowner becomes a surgical patient whose surgeon botches the operation, it may take a year or two for him to retain a lawyer and for the lawyer to file a lawsuit, and if the botch in question is a surgical sponge left in his gut, the year or two will not start to elapse until he discovers that fact, possibly several years after the operation.

Going to trial can easily not happen until five years after the suit is filed, and although the odds are that the suit will be settled, the settlement is most likely to be negotiated just before the trial is scheduled to begin. In those few cases that not only get tried but then get appealed, two or three years may expire before the appeals process is exhausted. The upshot is that medical malpractice insurance is unique in its excruciatingly long tail. The larger the amount of damages being claimed, the longer the tail is likely to be, because each side has a greater stake in fighting to the bitter end.

More concretely, a study commissioned by the American Insurance Association of roughly 10,000 malpractice claims closed in 1974 found that an average of thirteen months elapsed after the incident in dispute and before a claim was reported. The period between the incident and final disposition of the claim averaged thirty months, but if the figures were weighted by amount of the award, that average became forty-four months. After six years, close to 6 percent of the incidents were still unresolved, accounting for over

12 percent of the eventual total of award dollars paid out.[11] (It should be noted that the word "claim" in the malpractice category encompasses both lawsuits and actions short of litigation, such as the patient's lawyer calling the doctor to inform him that litigation is being considered and in effect inviting settlement negotiations. Some insurers even record a claim when a doctor or hospital reports to them an incident that they expect to become the subject of future litigation.)

What has made it necessary for a malpractice carrier to take the long-tail phenomenon into account is the fact that until 1975 malpractice insurance policies were always marketed on what is known as an occurrence basis. This simply means that what the carrier sells the doctor or hospital is protection against claims stemming from incidents occurring during the period covered by the policy (almost universally one year), regardless of when those incidents ripen into claims. Consequently, it has been the general practice of malpractice insurers to keep the accounts of a given policy year open for at least ten years thereafter.[12]

The long tail of malpractice insurance presents a carrier with a number of actuarial problems and one potential economic benefit. That potential benefit is simply that the ability to retain large numbers of premium dollars for a long period of time, if that period is an economically prosperous one complete with a bullish stock market, can become the ability to make heaps of investment income. There is evidence that this potential benefit has in the past been the critical incentive for many carriers to enter the field: The president of North American Reinsurance Corporation told a federal commission in 1972, for example, that "investment income actually derived from reserves held over very long periods seems to have its attractions to cash flow analysts in a few carriers now seeking to write more business of this class." [13] An Aetna representative told a Senate subcommittee in 1975: "If it were not for investment income, many companies would have discontinued writing medical malpractice insurance some years ago." [14]

The possibility of generous investment income held out by the long tail of malpractice insurance has been especially attractive to a carrier just beginning to underwrite that line. As a CNA executive wryly warned in a speech in 1972: "Recently a few more companies have re-entered the professional liability field. Their experience should be a happy one for a couple of years—all income, no out-go. But after those first few years, look out for that 'tail.' It can lash out with a vengeance." [15]

For the long tail to lash out means the coming true of an actuary's nightmare—unpredictability. Actuaries depend on predictability to set their prices, deciding what premiums to charge next year by looking at the claims experience of last year. But if most of the claims attributable to last year haven't even been reported yet, the actuary has to retreat further into the past for a data base from which to project. If the times are relatively stable in terms of the number and size (or "severity") of claims being filed, that procedure is reliable enough, but if both the frequency and the severity of claims have been accelerating rapidly, the long tail becomes a double bind. The further back the actuary goes for his data base, the less reliable the data become in terms of current experience; but the closer to the current year he gets, the less complete the data become in terms of encompassing all claims that will eventually be filed. [16]

The actuary's dilemma is accentuated by the fact that the largest claims are both the ones that take the longest to settle and the ones with the greatest potential for turning an underwriting profit into an underwriting loss if they were not anticipated in the pricing process. The situation becomes further complicated if increases in the number and size of claims being filed have something to do with changes in judge-made legal doctrines or in the group psychology of

juries, areas in which an actuary finds his predictive expertise to be more than a little inadequate.

Logically, then, the disadvantages to an insurer of the
long tail of the medical malpractice line would outweigh its
advantage if increasing numbers of claims were being filed
seeking increasingly large amounts of damages (presaging
underwriting losses due to pricing inadequacy) and/or if
the stock market was not doing well (presaging investment
losses). Psychologically, if not strictly logically, a booming
stock market might make the long tail's economic advantage
outweigh the perils of unpredictability on the decision-
making scales of at least some insurance carriers. It might
even make them somewhat casual about the soundness of
their prices. "I suspect that most of us would admit," said
one insurance executive in a speech to a trade association
meeting, "that rates, and especially liability rates, are actually not determined in a very scientific manner although
they are buttressed by a maze of charts, tables, graphs and
calculations. . . . Often enough, rates and trend factors
are worked backwards from competitive conditions to produce a lower result than might obtain from a pure statistical
approach." [17]

On the claims side of the equation, some observers trace
a significant increase in medical malpractice claims back to
the 1930's,[18] but most accounts of the growth in claims frequency and severity point to the late sixties as the significant
starting point. The data presented in such accounts, it should
be noted, are invariably impressionistic at best, for those
who might have kept useful statistics on the subject seem to
have made a point of not doing so.[19]

Prior to the crisis of the middle seventies, there was no
central source of data on malpractice claims or premiums.
Some carriers reported to a private statistical agent called
the Insurance Services Office, but many insurers, including
some major malpractice insurers, have not been affiliated

with ISO, and in any event, ISO's data are not necessarily reliable. ISO has not audited the data furnished it by carriers, and one case is reported in which a state insurance department considering a request for a rate increase found several errors in supporting ISO data.[20] Until 1976 state insurance departments did not require insurers to separate out malpractice claims data in the annual report insurers file with them, leaving such statistics to be buried in a category called liability other than auto.

Putting together bits and pieces of data from disparate sources has not always been possible, because such bits and pieces are frequently not comparable. An accurate overall picture of the rise in claims is impossible to compile, because what constitutes a claim has been defined differently by different insurers. The average size of payments made has also been defined in different ways. The computation of what a carrier calls an average loss payment may or may not include administrative expenses associated with handling the claim, and may or may not include cases in which no payment is made. ("The data will move around rather dramatically depending on the composition of the averages," according to an official of the American Insurance Association.[21])

At least two useful generalizations emerge from the data morass: all those statistical statements with which the malpractice debate has been littered deserve to be regarded with something less than reverence; and when loss allocation becomes a business, loss information can easily become a trade secret. Then, there is the fundamental problem that even if the quality of the historical data on malpractice claims were superb, such data (which is the most we could expect from the insurance industry) would tell us very little about either medical injuries or medical negligence, both categories that are undoubtedly larger (and ultimately more important) than the category of malpractice claims.

With all those caveats, it is perhaps worth mentioning a

few statistical tidbits as suggestive of the phenomenon of the accelerating frequency and expanding size of medical malpractice claims. Data from ISO on the frequency of claims reported against doctors (the number of claims per hundred insured doctors) from 1966 through 1973 show an erratic, mostly upward movement from 1966 to 1970 (an 11 percent increase from 1966 to 1967, a 5 percent decline from 1967 to 1968, a 15 percent increase from 1968 to 1969, and a 1 percent increase from 1969 to 1970), followed by sharp increases in the next three years (16 percent, 31 percent, and 29 percent). An industry authority reports that an unnamed hospital insurer not affiliated with ISO experienced stable claims frequencies from 1966 to 1970, with a rise in the 15 to 18 percent range for the following three years and a 30 percent rise for the first half of 1974.[22]

As to the expanding size of claims, the St. Paul Fire and Marine Insurance Company, a major malpractice insurer (covering over 48,000 doctors in 1974) that has found it expedient to release data on its claims experience, reports that the average cost of a claim (excluding administrative costs) rose by 87 percent between 1969 and 1974, from $6,705 to $12,534.[23] The malpractice insurance program of the New York State Medical Society (covering about half that state's physicians) experienced in that period a jump of 158 percent in the average payment per incident in which a payment was made, from $13,616 to $35,151.[24] (In terms of the problem of data comparability, it should be noted that the first source does not specify whether cases in which no payment was made are included in computing the average, whereas the second source does not specify whether administrative expenses associated with paying a claim are included in the average.)

The later sixties and early seventies saw three reactions by insurance carriers to claims increases, experienced and anticipated—raising premiums, leaving the field, and convincing themselves that group programs were the solution to the profitability problem. As to the first two, data on premiums and on carriers leaving and entering the field are as scattered and problematic as data on claims, so let us content ourselves with an offhand summary that appeared in the medical press in 1971: "Dozens of carriers have fled the malpractice market since the middle of the chaotic 1960s, and premiums across the country have zoomed by 50 to 800 percent." [25]

The growth of malpractice insurance programs associated with medical societies and hospital associations is no easier to describe with precision. A federally sponsored survey conducted in 1972 tells us generally that such plans "have grown substantially during the past five to ten years" [26] and that "the share of the total market sold to individual hospitals or practitioners, independent of any association or group sponsorship, has diminished rather markedly during the last five to eight years." [27] It enumerates thirty-seven state hospital associations and thirty-four state medical societies then sponsoring or endorsing group malpractice insurance programs.[28] (Such programs are not group insurance in the classic sense—in which the carrier writes a single master policy for the group and any member is automatically covered by it—but involve a state medical society or hospital association either actively negotiating and helping administer an insurance plan or simply endorsing a specific carrier's program.)

For the insurer the advantage of a group plan was the relatively easy (and administratively cheap) access it brought to large numbers of insureds and a generous volume of premium dollars, dollars that might include premiums for other lines of insurance that the carrier might also sell its new customers. The attraction of large premium volume was sufficiently compelling for that federal study to find in 1972 that "in contrast to the individual market, where many carriers have left the market or are passively accepting business, a number of carriers indicated that they are now actively seeking group business." [29]

Group coverage was held out to physicians as promising "an end to the vicious cycle of jumbo losses and escalating premiums." [30] *Medical Economics,* for example, told its doctor-readers in 1971: "Group programs bring into play a number of advantages over individual policies: administrative streamlining, premium pooling, and grass-roots peer review." [31] It proceeded to give several insurance executives space in its pages to sell the touted mutual advantages of a partnership between carrier and medical society, which for the carriers apparently included the assumption that committees of medical societies would be willing to exclude from society-sponsored insurance coverage their members who represented poor risks. On the other side, the physicians were apparently operating on the contradictory assumption that group coverage was their guarantee that the continued availability of malpractice insurance would not be a problem.[32] For this they later suffered such wrathful accusations from the insurance industry as that "the present [1975] predicament of the doctors is the result of years of abuse of the free-enterprise system. They are now paying the penalty of their years of monopolistic mass-marketing [sic] shopping for cheaper rates. Doing so they have virtually wiped out the voluntary markets." [33]

In the meantime, there was a period of confident optimism. A 1972 report of an industry advisory committee to the National Association of Insurance Commissioners found that "through the combined efforts of the medical societies, the insurers and the regulatory agencies, there has been a strengthening of the capability of the insurance market to handle malpractice problems, and a better understanding on the part of physicians of the nature of the difficulties being encountered by insurers." [34] A federal survey of the malpractice insurance market found the same year that "the

industry is recovering from its period of inadequate rates
during the mid and late 1960's." [35]

Such optimism may have had something to do with the
euphoria then prevailing in the larger industry. "The prop-
erty/liability industry," gushed *Best's Review,* a leading
trade magazine, in its annual roundup for 1972, "enters
1973 with the best two-year record it has ever compiled,
riding high in an economy which is expected to continue to
grow without being overpowered by inflation." [36] In mid-
1975, when euphoria had long since evaporated, *Best's*
would observe that "miscellaneous liability"—a catchall insurance category that includes medical malpractice—had
been a problem back in 1972, had in fact recorded a record
underwriting loss that year, but that such unpleasantness
had escaped much notice amid the general optimism inspired by record industry gains from both underwriting and
investment.[37]

In the two intervening years, elation became something
close to despair among property/liability insurance managements. On the underwriting side, profits of over $1 billion
in 1972 (in the property/liability insurance industry as a
whole) became zero in 1973 and then sank to a record underwriting loss of over $2 billion in 1974.[38] On the invest-
ment side, what one financial magazine called "the sick
stock market that prevailed in 1973 and 1974" [39] meant a
decline in the market value of the industry's stock portfolios
(otherwise known as realized and unrealized capital losses)
of about $4 billion in 1973 and $6 billion in 1974. These
horrendous portfolio losses both wiped out investment income (which was about $3 billion in 1973 and $3.5 billion
in 1974 [40]) and caused what is known in the trade as a
drain on surplus, surplus being a fund a carrier maintains to
draw on for loss payments if and when the premiums collected for that purpose turn out to be inadequate.

For market conditions to be causing a surplus shrinkage
at the same time that underwriting losses are having the

same effect is for an insurer a particularly unhappy state of affairs. A reduction in surplus eventually reduces the capacity of an insurer to underwrite business because the carrier lacks what it would regard as an adequate ratio of surplus to premiums. For this reason, several companies felt it necessary to dump a total of over $1 billion worth of stock during a declining market in 1974 to prevent further contraction of their surplus.[41]

A traumatized industry decided that something had to be done. "To discuss the present state of affairs as something that will, by the nature of the business itself, go away leaving barely a trace is dangerous wishful thinking," warned an industry leader in early 1975.[42] What was done was what some have called getting back to basics,[43] or rediscovering the insurance axiom that "if you don't have underwriting profit, you have nothing to work with when trouble comes." [44]

If a carrier's underwriting capacity is squeezed by a shrunken surplus, it is logical to sacrifice or limit those lines with the greatest risk of unprofitability. If investment gains no longer can be counted on to offset underwriting losses, it is logical to place renewed emphasis on the adequacy of premiums, which may mean raising them substantially. As it happens, such premium increases may be tantamount to getting out of the business altogether, for, as the president of the American Insurance Association put it, "Insurance companies cannot afford to write the insurance coverage for premiums that doctors and hospitals can afford to pay, and the health care practitioners and providers can't afford the premiums that clearly are warranted by the cost of claims." [45] Or, in the words of *Best's Review* in its roundup of 1975: "There are experienced and practical insurance men who have looked long and hard at the liability lines and concluded that their future is hopeless." [46]

The malpractice crisis thus erupted when an internal insurance industry problem was externalized, the carriers effecting what they saw as necessary readjustments in their way of doing business by announcing rate increases of unheard-of proportions and/or withdrawals from the market, all to the accompaniment of journalistic hyperbole decrying "a moral and monetary monster" [47] or "the mess that must be ended." [48] An industry position paper issued in late 1975 looked over the field and found that "whereas there was considerable competition among insurers in the 1960's to insure doctors, fewer than a dozen provide a significant market for this coverage today." [49]

The most conspicuous of the crisis-inducing carriers was the Argonaut Insurance Company, conspicuous not just because it had become one of the major malpractice insurers but also because its departure from the field was especially abrupt, reflecting the fact that its interest in malpractice insurance had been based on the attraction of a large cash flow combined with a bullish stock market. Argonaut started out, in 1957, as a workers' compensation insurer, and early on began furnishing liability insurance to some of the hospitals that were already its customers for compensation insurance.[50] In 1969 Argonaut was acquired by Teledyne, Inc., an aggressively expanding conglomerate, and in 1971 Teledyne decided that its new acquisition would enter the malpractice market in a big way.

Entering the malpractice market in a big way meant that by the end of that year, Argonaut had acquired a doctor clientele of 1,300, which became 14,000 by the end of 1973 and close to 30,000 by the end of 1974. It even gave the Florida Medical Society a 10 percent reduction in rates in 1973 for the privilege of taking over its malpractice program from an insurer that was bowing out because of excessive losses. Argonaut had also by 1974 become the chosen malpractice carrier of twenty-nine state hospital associations and was insuring about 25 percent of the nation's hospitals.

Teledyne apparently accepted the likelihood of underwriting losses from Argonaut's new thrust, but expected investment gains generated by all those premium dollars to bring it a net profit. That calculation was accurate in 1973, when Argonaut first experienced an underwriting loss but nonetheless chalked up a profit of over $18 million. But the next year the scheme went totally to pieces: Argonaut recorded a net operating loss (combining underwriting losses and investment income) of $105 million and on top of that suffered a loss from the sale of investments of $21 million, a drop of $91 million in the value of its remaining portfolio, and a decline in its surplus of $112 million.

Teledyne, which had not become a hot-shot conglomerate by slouching with its corporate feet on the desk, reacted decisively. In the fall of 1974 it fired most of Argonaut's top executives, and their replacements shortly began implementing a strategy of up or out, mostly out. The earliest and perhaps most conspicuous implementation of this strategy came in New York, where Argonaut had only just taken over the state medical society's program in July of 1974 (at a rate increase of 94 percent over the departing insurer's rates); in December it announced a 200 percent rate increase effective January 10, and when the state insurance department declined to cooperate, it huffily announced its departure from the state as of July 1, 1975. By later that summer a survey prepared for the American Bar Association was citing Argonaut's withdrawal from the malpractice market as having triggered a crisis in eight of the eleven states identified as problem areas.[51] In the meantime, Teledyne had announced in February that Argonaut's entry into the field had been a mistake and that in recognition of that fact Argonaut intended to discontinue covering doctors altogether and to insure a reduced number of hospitals at higher rates.

Teledyne's actions were a logical application of its management philosophy; as Teledyne's chairman and chief executive, Henry E. Singleton, explained in an interview with

Forbes: "We are conservatives. We placed survival first. Some companies don't, and you can see their wreckage all across the country. We have always carefully limited the degree of risk we undertake." [52] Carefully limiting risk is of course natural for private enterprises, for which survival means profitability, even if the business in question is the allocation of losses due to medical injuries. Teledyne's—and thereby Argonaut's—conduct may in particular instances have been atypically brash for the insurance industry, but that somewhat exaggerated manner only made clearer the underlying dynamic that was inevitably at work, whatever the public relations being conducted at the surface.

That underlying dynamic had to be a move toward greater predictability, because predictability in the aggregate is what makes the insurance industry possible. But what makes the insurance industry possible is not necessarily what makes an optimal system either of furnishing medical treatment or of compensating those who suffer adverse outcomes of medical treatment. The fact that the malpractice crisis was a crisis of insurance, not of medical practice—although the fundamental problem had to do with the growing tendency of patients to seek redress for perceived mistakes of medical practice—made it unlikely that the reactions it triggered would even begin to deal with the fundamental problem.

9

The Malpractice Debate
as Distortion

It is not physicians who are threatening to hold back coverage, but insurance companies. It is not physicians who are doubling and tripling premium rates but insurance companies. And it is not physician-defendants who are losing a majority of suits filed, but the plaintiffs—which indicates that many suits should not have been filed to begin with.
MALCOLM C. TODD, M.D.,
Past President, American Medical Association

Doctors cause the malpractice, not the lawyers. Doctors have to become more safety conscious. . . . Insurance companies are at fault. I think their rating practices need to be carefully examined. ROBERT E. CARTWRIGHT, ESQ.,
President, Association of Trial Lawyers of America

This really is not an insurance problem. It is a social problem. We find ourselves in the middle of it, but we do not feel that we caused it and we are not sure that anything really can be done within our particular industry to make the basic changes that have to be effectuated. WARREN COOPER,
Vice President and Actuary, Chubb & Son, Inc.

THE malpractice crisis as insurance crisis spawned what had the trappings of a public debate on the malpractice issue but what on closer inspection was mostly a disjointed collection of self-interested pronouncements issuing from those whose stake in the public perception of the issue was matched by their ease of access to the media—doctors, lawyers, and, to a lesser extent, insurers. Doctors and lawyers were equally preoccupied with defending the sanctity of their respective professional turfs, while the insurers were scurrying to find a way off the battlefield altogether. The interests of patients were either entirely ignored or else were co-opted by the malpractice lawyers, who found it expedient to use the rhetoric of concern for the victims to conceal the reality of concern for maintaining the profitability of representing them.

The media, for which reports from the front are more profitable than independent contemplative analyses, were for the most part only too willing to pass on the misleading and partial statistics, half-truths and exaggerations, self-righteousness and paranoia that became the typical mode of discourse on the malpractice phenomenon. Occasionally the working press did perform the public service of letting the hot air out of one of the protagonists' balloons. *The New York Times,* for example, at one point reported on a press release put out by a public-relations firm representing the New York County Medical Society by noting that, while the release deplored an 850 percent increase in one hospital's malpractice insurance premiums, it had neglected to mention that the hospital had tripled its basic coverage, extended it to several additional employees, and bought extra insurance beyond the basic coverage.[1] Such an independent assessment of a blast in the war of words was, however, an exceptional event, and in any case failed to steer the discussion in a direction approaching the concerns of the patients-turned-litigants.

Instead, the direction taken by the debate was shaped by the explosive outrage of the medical profession that the insurance industry dared to treat it like any other losing proposition: "The insurance industry, with a few exceptions, has failed miserably in representing both physicians and the public. . . . Instead of proposing solutions when the going got hot, the *industry turned and ran.* [Emphasis in the original.] Of little concern to them was the fact that doctors would be left totally unprotected and that society would be left without physicians to care for them."[2] That was the accusation of the Physicians Crisis Committee, a group of surgeons and anesthesiologists in Detroit.

What advocates for physicians tended to ignore was that such statements, in implying that doctors left without insurance would refuse to treat patients, assumed that the medical profession is entitled to a preferred economic position in society. While complaining, that is, of the irresponsibility of the insurance industry in declining to take on what insurers regard as an excessive economic risk, such a statement finds it natural for members of the medical profession to decline to take the economic risk of treating patients without having insurance protection against their legal liability for unhappy results of treatment.

But the ire of the doctors did not dwell on the carriers— possibly because they were quick to point out that the increase in claims was no doing of theirs—but soon moved on to the legal profession and its operating theater, the common-law courts. The lawyers would have preferred to avoid any public scrutiny of their operations and incomes. "In 1975," one of them complained, "in order to attract public attention to an issue, special interest groups, the press, or those seeking immunity or limitation of their accountability [read "physicians"] enjoy the use of the word 'crisis' for any problem that happens to be a source of irritation financially or otherwise." [3]

Once under attack, however, the malpractice bar showed its adversary skills to be equal to any in the production of accusations that were as overblown as they were pointed. Like the doctors, the lawyers took potshots at the insurance industry—in one statement accusing it of "a nationwide concerted drive . . . to panic the doctors, and to wipe out the rights of the ultimate consumer who may be a victim of someone's negligence" [4]—but concentrated their fire on the members of the other profession.

For their part, the insurers, who faulted both the doctors for having patients whose treatment was unsuccessful and the lawyers for taking them on as clients, found the most comfortable position to be a retreat to the safety of platitudes—usually variations on the theme of it's really a medical/legal/social problem, not an insurance problem at all. They were right, of course, but their rightness reflected less a sincere concern with root causes than an ardent desire to maintain their freedom of action without interference from hostile outsiders.

The multiplicity and diversity of charges and countercharges spewed forth by doctors and lawyers tended to cluster around two issues of acute interest to any modern professional—compensation and competence. The doctors took the offensive on the compensation issue, with one poll finding that a majority of physicians saw "fee-happy" lawyers as a major contributing cause of the malpractice crisis and that 25 percent considered them the leading cause.[5] Doctors found a convenient target in a compensation mechanism that they wouldn't dream of using but that has become the predominant American system of financing malpractice and other personal-injury litigation—the contingent fee. This arrangement gives the lawyer a percentage (usually a third to a half) of any settlement or judgment the case brings, but no compensation if the case is lost; payment of the fee, in other words, is contingent on a successful outcome.

At least some doctors found the key to the malpractice crisis to be the trial lawyers' need for new contingent-fee business as the spread of no-fault auto insurance reduced the supply of accident cases. "The plaintiff's bar has contributed to the malpractice crisis by filing an exceptionally large number of malpractice cases since the advent of no-fault automobile insurance," concluded the Physicians Crisis Committee.[6] Other physicians concluded more generally that the problem was with lawyers who had found malpractice litigation to be a potential gold mine: "Basically, what attracts lawyers into the field of litigation is the fact that the amount of money doled out is based more on the imagined ability of the system to pay than on what the injury is worth." [7]

For the lawyers the obvious line of counterattack was to question the motives of their accusers and to present themselves as champions of the rights of the underdog. "It ill behooves the single most affluent sector of our society to complain about the fees earned by lawyers," huffed one trial lawyers' organization.[8] "There is a certain segment of the medical profession," charged another, "who would wish to deprive innocent victims of careless medical treatment of their right to be compensated to the extent that money can ever compensate loss of health and well-being." [9]

Accompanying the pointed lance was the shield and the shining armor: "The contingency [sic] fee system is the only means by which people can be assured of an opportunity to have the very best attorney handle their injury case. This is especially critical in the area of the seriously injured patient who could not possibly afford to hire an attorney but who most desperately needs access to the courts." [10]

The doctors' condemnation of the contingent fee as an incentive to sue glossed over the fact that the contingent feature tends to operate as a crude quality-control device— lawyers who know their stuff (malpractice specialists, in other words) will reject cases that look doubtful because they represent a risk that their labor will go uncompensated. (There was something to the argument of one lawyer that "it might be better if we had a contingency [sic] fee for doctors, where they would be paid only if the operation was a success. It might make doctors more careful." [11]) And the doctors equally ignored the fact that even a case involving a relatively blameless doctor taken on by a maximally greedy lawyer reflects a situation in which a patient both perceives himself as medically injured and is angry enough about it to sue.

The contingent-fee system does, however, suffer from a serious deficiency—but it is a deficiency that the medical profession had no interest in making an issue of. Below a threshold amount of monetary damages—the figure of $20,000 has frequently been cited [12]—a percentage of the recovery does not represent a large enough return on the necessary investment of time for a malpractice lawyer to be willing to take the case, no matter how clear-cut the medical negligence. The contingent fee thus skews the legal system in favor of those who are permanently disabled (and will incur long-term medical expenses) and/or have had high earnings (lost earnings representing a significant proportion of damages in malpractice suits); it discriminates against those who were either only temporarily injured and/or whose earning potential was limited.

If the trial lawyers were on the defensive on the compensation issue, they went on the offensive on the issue of competence: "The sole cause of medical malpractice cases *is* medical malpractice." [13] Or in a slightly more sophisticated version: "Malpractice cases are created by a few negligent doctors, not by lawyers. The number of malpractice cases reflects the amount of negligent treatment to which the public is being subjected by these negligent doctors." [14]

Not only is there an equivalence between malpractice litigation and negligent physician performance, but, the argument of the malpractice bar continued, such litigation serves to make the physician accountable to the patient: "The 'crisis' referred to in the press by the American Medical Association, or other associated special interest groups, is in fact a realization that, after uncountable years of unaccountability, the medical profession has suddenly become 'accountable' for its transgressions with the rest of mankind." [15]

Finally, the argument wound up, suing the doctor not only brings the patient redress but also serves the socially useful purpose of improving the quality of medical care: "The tort lawsuit is the victim's only effective weapon for obtaining justice and society's only means of forcing the improvement of medical care." [16] (A tort is the civil equivalent of a criminal offense, i.e., conduct that the common-law courts have determined entitles its victims to redress through a civil lawsuit.) "In the area of medical malpractice, perhaps more than in any other single field, the plaintiffs' trial bar can point to an unequaled record of contributing to the protection of the public by compelling scrutiny and improvement of the medical profession." [17] This effort is especially critical, it was urged, because the medical profession's record of self-regulation is beneath contempt: "An attorney can be disbarred, an Army Officer drummed out of the corps and a priest unfrocked. The doctors don't even have a name for it." [18]

For the doctors, needless to say, such arguments made little sense. "Something is wrong. It is not because we are practicing inferior medicine, or America would not be the medical mecca of the world. Our [legal] system is at fault." [19] That system, the argument went, was placing unfair burdens on the medical profession: "The basic problem really arises from the fact that society has chosen to pay for medical disabilities regardless of cause with a malpractice insurance dollar." [20] "It is unfair for the system to expect medicine to compensate for patients who contribute to their own injury through carelessness, by failing to follow instructions, or poor personal habits. . . . No longer can providers of medicine be expected to solve society's psychological and socioeconomic problems." [21]

On the other hand, one rebuttal to the argument that malpractice suits are a form of quality control acknowledged the existence of incompetent doctors but claimed that lawyers liked them that way: "There is no known lawyer who on winning malpractice cases turns around and gives his evidence to the District Attorney or State Board of Medical

Education and Licensure to have physicians removed from practice. Indeed, quite the reverse is correct because it is to the advantage of the practicing lawyer to keep the physician in practice who does indeed engage in negligent practice for therein lies the source of income for that lawyer." [22]

The problem with the lawyers' simple equation of malpractice cases with malpractice—as many doctors were quick to point out—was that it failed to explain why the rate of litigation was greater in places like California and New York than, say, in North Dakota or Vermont, where one would expect the clinical level of medical practice to be less advanced. The lawyers' argument similarly failed to deal with the fact that at least some of the doctors being sued were impressively credentialed and highly regarded superspecialists. The medical profession, on the other hand, was unwilling to consider the possibility that *something* might be wrong with the medical system in such clinically advanced localities and with the practice of such expert superspecialists, something wrong that was being reflected in such large numbers of patients who were both injured enough and angry enough to sue their doctors.

The problem with the trial lawyers' glorification of tort law and the judicial system was that it failed to acknowledge the frustrating and inequitable realities of that system for the patient-litigant—the de facto lack of redress when an injured patient can only claim a few thousand dollars in damages; the lack of any form of redress other than money paid long after the fact; the burden on the patient to recognize his injury and the possibility of medical negligence and to seek out legal representation; the excruciating delays; the irrationalities in determining the amount of a jury award or negotiated settlement, much of which goes in any event to the lawyer and his expert witnesses. Some of the medical counterattacks on the legal profession made the point well: "In the search for some kind of 'finite justice,' society has allowed the lawyers to create a system filled with red tape, motions, depositions, appeals, adjournments, and delay that is simply too expensive to bear. Obviously the main beneficiaries of such a system are the lawyers." [23] But such concern with the inequities and inefficiencies of the judicial system, it should quickly be noted, had never been voiced by the medical profession until that system became visibly more receptive to suits brought by patients against their doctors and hospitals.

Even were an individual patient as plaintiff content to weather the intricacies of litigation for the sake of serving as a quality-control device, and even granting instances where malpractice suits have served as an incentive to effect technical improvements in medical treatment, the same inefficiencies and irrationalities of malpractice litigation as patient recompense apply equally to malpractice litigation as quality control. More problematically, the whole legalistic perspective on the malpractice crisis—that malpractice suits reflect individual incompetent physicians and conversely are a mechanism for raising the level of individual physician competence—rests on a narrow view of what has been happening that might be called the bad-apple theory.

In whatever context it comes up, the bad-apple theory always has a ring of plausibility, because it always seems self-evident that a small percentage of whomever—butchers, bakers, or candlestick makers—will be incompetent, immoral, criminal, or whatever negative adjective fits the problem under discussion. That plausibility then usually develops into a huge sense of relief among those concerned with the problem, relief that its cause has been identified as something localized and therefore presumably manageable.

Both doctors and lawyers have found that kind of relief—and even a convergence of opinion, if and when they stop screaming at each other long enough to realize it—in the bad-apple theory of doctors and of lawyers. The trial lawyers, that is to say, have been willing to admit that a few of their number have been known to file baseless lawsuits, while the doctors have for their part been willing to admit that some members of their profession don't do very well at practicing medicine. In both cases what quickly follows the admission is the old saw about babies and their bathwater. In the case of some of the more sophisticated medical groups the admission has been accompanied by a plea for legislation to reinforce the power of the profession to banish its bad apples from practice.[24]

Such a strategy obviously has a lot to do with a desire by professionals to keep control of the profession in their own hands. But even where the function of bad-apple elimination is given to some external agency, the fact that the problem is described in those terms is a critical victory for modern medicine. For while admitting to blemishes, this view of the problem leaves the underlying system of medical practice intact and under control. An alternative view of the problem as pervading the structure and function of modern medical practice would—to extend the metaphor—threaten to upset the entire apple cart. Thus, rotten apples become convenient scapegoats, and dealing with the problem they represent—which, however real, is only a part of the problem the malpractice phenomenon reflects—becomes a diversionary maneuver to avoid confronting the fundamental sources of patient dissatisfaction.

10

The Malpractice Crisis
as Vicious Circle

I have a list above the phone of suit-prone patients who are not to be given appointments.

An unnamed general practitioner
quoted in a poll taken by *Medical Economics*

Don't hesitate to ask for a consultation whenever that's appropriate. If there is to be trouble, don't get into it alone.

MICHAEL E. ARNOFF, M.D., an otolaryngologist,
writing in *Medical Economics*

"BEING sued by a patient, for whom the physician has developed an attachment and for whom he has done his best, is a devastating occurrence. . . . A court of law may be the workroom for the attorney, but it is the torture chamber for the doctor." Whether appropriate or pathological, the extreme intensity of physicians' emotional reaction to the fact of patients suing their doctors has been undeniable. (The quoted remark was made by an orthopedic surgeon speaking at a conference on malpractice held in 1975.[1]) Even as filtered by the processes of publication, that reaction has sometimes bordered on anguish: "The doctor feels put upon. He feels nude on the corner of the Main Street of life. He often tries to cover himself with pride and even occasional arrogance, only to find himself being castrated. He really doesn't want to believe the hostility he feels, and often interprets it as being greater than it is." (That statement appeared in 1973, in the back pages of the report of a federal commission.[2])

Lawyers revel in a hostile clash of wits, regarding the

hostility as merely part of the game and never to be taken as a personal affront. But for doctors, grappling with inevitable uncertainty as much as with disease and death, the prospect of criticism brings with it intolerable vulnerability. "The physician's attitudes are marked by a profound ambivalence. On the one side he has a more than ordinary sense of uncertainty and vulnerability; on the other, he has a sense of virtue and pride, if not superiority. This ambivalence is expressed by sensitivity to criticism by others. In most cases he is prone to feel that he is above reproach, that he did his best and cannot be held responsible for untoward results." [3]

The problem of uncertainty combines with the need for the emotional sustenance that patients are expected to provide; "in a somewhat paradoxical way the doctor is dependent on the patient and particularly on the patient's dependency." [4] Criticism from a patient is akin to betrayal: "This anger of some physicians at the increased malpractice rates and the increased frequency of suits is surely understandable . . . for such suits remind them that they do make mistakes and, more important, that they are not always loved." [5]

Criticism delivered privately by a professional colleague, who shares the problem of uncertainty and the need for patient dependency, may be grudgingly accepted, its legitimacy, at least in principle, acknowledged. But socially legitimated judgment (a particularly powerful form of criticism) handed down by a body that is defined precisely by its lack of professional expertise—a jury—is perceived by doctors as the ultimate affront. The fact that the vast majority of malpractice claims are settled before trial and that the vast majority of those that do reach a jury are decided in the doctor's favor [6] is all apparently irrelevant to the hurt, resentment, and self-pity of the physician as self-anointed victim of what one medical magazine has called "medicine's King Kong." [7] And although at least one physician-commentator has observed that "counseling for the physician who is being sued might be helpful," [8] it is more likely that the emotional trauma of a suit—or even of merely feeling vulnerable to suit—will be left to fester, ultimately to poison the atmosphere of all the doctor's encounters with patients, most of whom have no advance inclination to be critical, much less litigious.

Resentment and wounded pride, transmuted into anxious hostility, create a sort of psychic overkill, expressed in a varied collection of strategies aimed at neutralizing in advance the threat of the patient-as-potential-litigant. In the growing body of literature bemoaning, analyzing, and pontificating about the malpractice issue, this strategic posture has come to be called defensive medicine. Whatever its objective content (and one practitioner's defensive practice may be another's long-standing routine), the defining characteristic of defensive medicine is a subjective concern less with which response to the patient's distress is most likely to relieve it than with which techniques of diagnosis and treatment will constitute the most unassailable defense to a charge of malpractice. The patient of course is not tipped off that he is now being viewed as a potential enemy whose well-being has become a secondary consideration; thus, defensive medicine is inherently deceptive medicine.

Broadly speaking, defensive medicine usually means more of the same—more lab tests, more X rays, more assorted other diagnostic procedures, more hospitalization, more consultations and referrals, more formulating what is wrong with the patient in terms of what is reflected in objectified indications. Sometimes it means less in one sense, more in another—fewer general practitioners willing to deliver babies or fewer general surgeons willing to repair broken bones, with more specialization of practice as a result. It may simply reinforce the general attitude of activism that shapes modern medical practice: "The physician has always hated to miss a lesion even if he could do nothing for it; to

professional pride is now added the fear that if he does not
do everything, someone may say that he has not exercised
professional duty with sufficient zeal." [9] At the same time,
the incentives of fee-for-service mesh nicely with the incentives of defensiveness; the extra follow-up visit, just to be
absolutely sure that things look good (and to get that fact
on the medical record) brings with it, after all, an additional fee.

The extreme of defensive medicine as retaliation for the
threat of criticism-by-litigation is its use as a form of black-
mail in the public forum. This stance begins with the assumption that defensive medicine is compulsory. Under the
heading "The Frightening Truth," for example, a legal reference for doctors claims: "In this age of consumerism, even
the most knowledgeable and thorough doctor is compelled
to practice 'defensively.' He is performing additional tests,
carrying out additional diagnostic procedures—just to be
on the safe side of any eventual malpractice suit." [10] At this
point in the argument some advocates for medicine feel it
necessary to counteract charges that defensive medicine is
an undesirable development. An article prepared for the
Office of Legal Counsel of the American Medical Association, for example, is itself a study in defensiveness: "Undoubtedly, the desire to avoid malpractice liability is a
motivating factor that induces some physicians to order
laboratory tests. If the test is beneficial, however, the motive
is immaterial. . . . The desire for protection from malpractice claims may lead some physicians to order hospitalization or consultations in some instances in which
they would not otherwise do so. When this happens, it
causes no harm to the patient and may obviate potential
problems." [11]

Defensive-medicine-as-blackmail emerges when the stance
is taken that the practice does have unfortunate aspects—
all those extra tests do increase the cost of medical care, at
least [12]—but that the only way to ameliorate the problem is

for society at large to eliminate the possibility of doctors being sued. In the words of an article by a general surgeon in Denver: "The present climate is such that we cannot stop the practice of 'defensive medicine.' We will not be able to do this until the public understands what is happening to it. So long as the physician feels threatened by the courts—whether the threat is real or imagined—he is going to respond by protecting himself." [13] The article neglects to explain how the public can alleviate a threat that is powerful even when imaginary, and it ignores the fact that society usually takes a dim view of people who shape their conduct in reaction to imaginary threats. More important, it implicitly rejects the possibility of a reexamination of the form and content of the doctor-patient encounter as a means of attempting to cope with the problem reflected in the malpractice phenomenon.

A number of professional organizations and publications have sought to answer the question of how prevalent the practice of defensive medicine really is. Their approach, as one would expect, has been to conduct a poll. While the precise figures produced by such efforts do not warrant being taken very seriously—the methodology of some of them is probably subject to criticism, and the ability of people dispassionately to analyze their motivations in the context of such an emotionally charged issue is in any event questionable—it is worth noting their findings for the sense they provide of a professional mentality that has apparently become common, if not prevalent.

A poll conducted early in 1977 by the AMA's Center for Health Services Research and Development (in which 111 of a sample of 500 physicians responded to a questionnaire) found that 93 percent of the respondents were more aware than they had been that they might be sued for malpractice and that 76 percent were practicing defensive medicine, defined as "ordering extra tests and procedures for patients as a protection against potential malpractice suits." Asked whether they thought other doctors were practicing defensively, 80 percent thought that over half their colleagues were, including 29 percent who believed that all doctors were doing it.[14]

The Medical Society of Virginia collected questionnaires in 1976 from 2,700 of its members (52 percent of the total), of which 73 percent said they were ordering additional X rays and tests for defensive purposes.[15] The Auditor General of California in 1975 surveyed a sample of the members of the California Medical Association (274 of a sample of 540 responded); 59 percent said that "the current situation" had caused them to make more frequent use of lab tests, X rays, consultations, and hospitalization, which in many cases they felt to be medically unnecessary.[16] (One should probably not jump to the conclusion that physicians in Virginia are more anxious than their colleagues in California; the difference probably has at least something to do with the difference between 1975 and 1976 and with the inherent amorphousness of the issue.)

Back in 1974 *Medical Economics* sent questionnaires to a random national sample of practicing physicians (receiving responses from 1,407 of a sample of 4,020), asking sixteen questions about possible changes in the respondents' practice habits as a result of "concern over legal liability." Over 80 percent of the respondents checked off at least one such change; 48 percent (the largest proportion for any of the sixteen items) indicated that they were ordering more diagnostic tests.[17]

The surgeons got a head start as pollsters—perhaps reflecting their particular vulnerability to suit—when the American College of Surgeons collected questionnaires from about 15,000 of its fellows in 1972. These asked whether the respondent's practice had been modified by the malpractice problem in any of several specified ways; 61 percent replied that they were ordering X rays more frequently, and 53 percent said that they were using more lab tests.[18]

Besides subjecting the patient to additional technological manipulations, defensive medicine may involve being more compulsive about getting it all on the record. The *Medical Economics* poll, for example, drew the comment from an ophthalmologist that "I put in [the record] things of no medical significance because they might be useful in a suit." And an endocrinologist pouted, "I treat the chart more than the patient, with one eye out for ambulance-chasing lawyers." With or without comment, 44 percent of the poll's participants said that they were making more detailed entries on office and hospital records as a form of malpractice protection.[19] Of the surgeons responding to the American College of Surgeons survey, 55 percent said that they were "amplifying" their records because of the malpractice problem.[20]

As well as being more technological and more documented, defensive medicine may be more fragmented and superspecialized medicine. This results when defensiveness is expressed by the physician's either seeking a consultation (calling in another physician for his opinion) or making a referral (sending the patient off to another, more specialized or differently specialized, physician). Forty percent of the respondents to the *Medical Economics* poll said that they were getting more consultations, including one general surgeon who explained, "I use consultations even when they're not necessary, simply to impress the patient." [21] Referrals were being made more frequently by 31 percent of the respondents, including another surgeon who was referring "everything that is not in my specialty, even if it's simple and I could manage it." Patients with bone problems being sent off to orthopedic surgeons (even by general surgeons) and those with heart problems being referred to cardiologists (even by internists) were found to be the most common types of referrals.[22]

Finally, 30 percent of those polled had stopped performing certain procedures altogether, implying that such services were being furnished by more specialized practitioners instead. These included pediatricians "eliminating anything even peripherally related to surgery," ophthalmologists refusing to perform cosmetic surgical repairs, and general surgeons staying away from a whole range of procedures, especially those involving bones. Even subspecialists were becoming more specialized; plastic surgeons, for example, were referring hand cases to subsubspecialists, while orthopedic surgeons were doing the same with candidates for total hip replacements.[23] The American College of Surgeons poll found in 1972 that 51 percent of its respondents were using consultations more frequently and that 21 percent were limiting their practice, primarily by not performing certain procedures.[24]

The Virginia survey reported that 42 percent of its respondents said "they can no longer afford to treat patients considered to be 'high risk' because of the nature of their illnesses." [25] A 1976 Rand Corporation study of changes in practice made by California physicians in response to rising malpractice insurance premiums found "fragmentary evidence that family physicians have increasingly been referring obstetrical and surgical patients to specialists and that specialists no longer performing certain procedures are referring patients to those who do." [26] A Rand survey of third-year family-practice residents in California asked whether they expected to be doing fewer procedures such as obstetrics, surgery, orthopedics, and anesthesia as a result of the malpractice crisis; 92 percent of the responses were affirmative.[27]

Closely allied to both technology and superspecialization as manifestations of defensiveness is the practice of more readily putting patients in the hospital, where technology and consultants are always at hand. Of the respondents to the *Medical Economics* survey, 18 percent were hospitalizing more patients for defensive purposes, including a general practitioner who had taken to admitting patients with mild pneumonia and an orthopedist who was hospitalizing patients with simple back strain. For some doctors, hospitalization, like consultation, was a way of spreading responsibility around; one ophthalmologist, for example, said he hospitalized patients for minor procedures because "I want plenty of company." [28] The trend is being encouraged by such sources of medicolegal advice as *Medical Economics*'s own "Practice Management" column, which in one issue advised a worried surgeon who, at his patient's insistence, had performed a minor procedure in the office: "When you have any doubts about performing a particular operation in your office, don't do it." [29]

It must be admitted that some instances of defensive medicine probably represent technical improvements in medical practice. The risk of brain damage from cardiac arrest on the operating table, for example, has apparently been lessened for surgical patients in California since a jury found in effect that anything less than continuous monitoring of the pulse of a patient under anesthesia was malpractice.[30] But the increased use of diagnostic procedures that seems to be the most common manifestation of defensiveness would logically be creating an increase in the overall level of patient risk. All those polls spewing out percentages of doctors practicing defensively have tended to avoid this issue, although back in 1971 a law professor who interviewed seventeen assorted specialists in the Pittsburgh area reported that they were experiencing "mixed" results from defensively ordering additional diagnostic procedures. "Although some latent disease processes are uncovered early, the yield is very low, and there is the added risk of iatrogenic disease." [31] The risk involved in the promiscuous use of X rays inspired a sardonic reply by a radiologist to the *Medical Economics* survey: "Some day, some patient is going to sue her physician for exposing her unnecessarily to too much radiation." [32]

On the related practice of defensively putting patients in

the hospital, the commentary that accompanied the results of that survey warned that defensively hospitalizing patients not seriously ill rested on "a shaky premise" because "a lot of people actually seem to get well faster at home." Besides, it added, "there may even be more chance that a patient will start looking for a lawyer if something goes wrong while he's in the hospital. An institutional setting can magnify the gravity of a medical error or a blameless bad result." [33] Defensiveness, in short, can exacerbate the situation that created the breeding ground for suits by patients against doctors in the first place.

But if a link between defensive medicine and intensified risk is necessarily speculative, a direct connection between defensiveness and intensified doctor-patient hostility is undeniable. For whatever else it involves, defensive medicine means that the doctor views the patient not as an object of altruistic concern but as a potential antagonist to be outwitted in advance. "I look at every patient as a potential malpractice suit when she first enters my office," an obstetrician-gynecologist wrote in response to the *Medical Economics* poll.[34] Outwitting in some cases means outright rejection, effected in a maximally formalized way: "If after a few visits you sense hostility or resistance that you can't overcome," advises an article on avoiding malpractice suits, "terminate the doctor-patient contact without further ado. Send the patient a certified letter telling him what you're doing and what arrangements you'll make for equivalent coverage. And be sure to request a return receipt." [35]

Another doctor recommends certified mail as self-protection if a patient fails to keep an appointment for a blood test to check the effects of long-term medication: "If they fail to honor their appointments, I advise them—by certified mail —of the medical consequences of *their* negligence." [36] This scenario illustrates how comparable objective actions can have diametrically opposite subjective meanings; a doctor writing a patient who missed an appointment, that is to say, may either be expressing concern for what neglect of his condition may mean to the patient or be shedding responsibility for the patient's care while making sure that his legal flanks are covered. A patient, we may be sure, is readily able to distinguish one motivation from the other. Thus, patient hostility, of which doctors constantly complain, can become a self-fulfilling prophecy—the patient coming to the doctor with a desire to trust, being met with a screen of suspicion and wariness, and inevitably feeling resentment that in his search for an ally he has been branded an enemy.

Even conveying information to the patient about his condition and the possibilities for dealing with it can be an expression of either concern or hostility. The patient, that is to say, may be implicitly informed that the doctor views him as properly a participant in the getting-better process or may sense that the doctor is manipulating him into freeing the doctor from the possibility of blame. The latter situation is illustrated by an excerpt from a letter to the editor from a group of distinguished academic physicians: "The public must face the fact that there is no harmless or fool-proof medical procedure. . . . Moreover, when the individual takes the chance to obtain a potential medical benefit after he has been properly informed of the benefits and the risks, he automatically shares responsibility with all those who provide and administer the agent." [37] (The "agent" alluded to was the swine flu vaccine; the fact that the letter dealt with that controversy rather than with the malpractice issue makes it no less illustrative of the defensive posture that has come to be an outstanding characteristic of the medical profession.)

Physicians responding to the California Auditor General's survey noted the effects that defensiveness makes inevitable: "a deterioration in the doctor-patient relationship due to increased mutual suspicion; a reluctance by physicians to take risky cases; and an increased tendency on the part of physicians to view patients as potential adversaries." [38] Defensiveness does nothing to break the causal chain linking objective risk and subjective alienation to the nexus of injury and anger that triggers a malpractice claim; defensiveness instead, by magnifying the psychological distance between doctor and patient, precludes the possibility of their jointly groping for a common understanding of what should be a mutual plight. Defensiveness, in short, transforms the malpractice crisis into a vicious circle.

11

The Futility of Official Responses

As individuals, doctors are terrific lobbyists. They convey authority, power and dogma. . . . They successfully bully individual legislators. And they have something else which is apparent in talking to legislators who are diabetic or have a history of coronaries. They are scared of doctors because they are scared about their own doubtful longevity.

DAVID M. KINZER,
"Laws on Order: Confessions of a Lobbyist"

"Explain all that," said the Mock Turtle.
"No, no! The adventures first," said the Gryphon in an impatient tone: "explanations take such a dreadful time."
LEWIS CARROLL, *Alice's Adventures in Wonderland*

"THE liability tort reform measures enacted into law in the past two years could stand alone as a remarkable record of achievement." So trumpeted a report prepared for the December 1976 meeting of the American Medical Association's Board of Trustees.[1] In terms of quantity, this self-glorification was not off the mark. In the two years 1975 and 1976 the legislatures of forty-nine states plus Puerto Rico and the Virgin Islands responded to the malpractice crisis by enacting over 250 pieces of legislation that could be advertised as constituting "malpractice reform."[2] (Only Montana and the District of Columbia stayed off the bandwagon.) One legal commentator called it "a flood of legislation, a torrent unparalleled . . . in the history of medical law in this country."[3]

The essentially fortuitous timing of the crisis happened to

synchronize well with the legislative process. The insurance companies dropped their bombshells of outrageous premium increases or withdrawals from the malpractice market by early in 1975, before the 1975 legislative sessions had had time to get bogged down in other business. The premium increases and withdrawals were mostly to be effective July 1, which lent a sense of urgency to the issue but which in most cases gave the legislatures the rest of their session in which to take action.[4]

Organized medicine can take credit for being the catalyst and prime mover behind the avalanche of malpractice legislation. Bolstered by consultant services from the AMA, state medical societies imposed special assessments on their memberships (in about twenty states), hired public-relations firms (two were retained by the state society in New York), and began pouring on a barrage of paper. Brochures and bill stuffers were the favored propaganda medium; these were directed not at legislators directly but at patients, in whom their messages were intended to induce panic that lack of insurance might put their doctor out of business—to be followed by the insistence that their elected representatives *do* something immediately. As one California legislator observed: "Perhaps one of the most significant political forces involved in the medical malpractice crisis was the ability of local doctors to arouse their patients and have those patients *demand* substantial reform." [5] Doctors themselves in many states descended by the busload on the legislative halls, and in a few (notably California and New York, to a lesser extent Texas and Indiana) took the heretofore unthinkable step of going on strike (or some euphemistic equivalent).[6]

That the malpractice crisis was catalyzed by an insurance upheaval, threatening to make insurance unavailable or unaffordable, determined the thrust of the lobbying and the legislation that resulted. The typical legislative package combined the creation of insurance mechanisms for resolv-

ing the availability problem with an agglomeration of manipulations of the legal system, justified by the theory that
they would eventually make possible a reduction in (or at
least a moderation in the increase of) malpractice insurance
premiums. These manipulations could be categorized as involving the imposition of limitations on recovery of damages by patients, changes in the tort law determining patients' right to recover at all, and/or changes in the formal
mechanisms for resolving claims of malpractice.

In many states the legislators thought it advisable to
balance their enactments by extracting a quid pro quo from
the medical profession in the form of tightening the process
of physician licensing and discipline. This approach was
sometimes seen as a variation of the divide-and-conquer
strategy; in the words of the sponsor of the California legislation, "By pitting the various concerned and powerful interest groups against one another, while preserving the
delicate balance among them, we had a better chance of
getting something out. This is called the 'equal bite'
theory." [7]

The narrow origins of the crisis also meant that once
legislators had given the doctors a way to get insurance and
something to quell their urgent cries for "tort law reform,"
they could assure themselves that they had done their duty
and conquered the problem. In the words of a Wisconsin
legislator, "As in many other states, Wisconsin's medical
malpractice 'crisis' lasted for a 6-month period . . . and
then faded away with the passage of comprehensive legislation." [8] By the fall of 1976, the staffs of state medical societies were bemoaning the apathy of state officials on the
malpractice issue. "The governor, the insurance commissioner, and the legislators seem to feel they have fulfilled
their obligation with the passage of A.B. 1," complained a
staff member of the California Medical Association.[9] Not
that the medical societies were looking for systemic changes
in the bases of medical practice, but they were correct in

sensing that the extent of legislative action was too superficial to make much difference in the long run.

It is probably too much to expect of state legislators that
they rise above their traditional role of juggling the competing demands of special-interest groups with the aim of
offending none of them, if possible, or only the least powerful, if not. (A hospital-association lobbyist once described
the state legislator as "the 'man in the middle' of a society in
conflict." [10]) Typically, the most that legislative bodies find
themselves able to do by way of dealing with the root causes
of serious social problems is to appoint some sort of study
commission, a maneuver that forty-seven states employed
on the malpractice question.[11] As for the so-called malpractice reform laws, the best that can be said for them is that
they temporarily turned an acute crisis back into a chronic
problem. The legislators' charge through the malpractice
arena left behind both the prospect that a renewed crisis
would break through the fragile repairs they had thrown together and the inevitability that the underlying problem
would continue to erode the social consensus supporting the
structure of medical practice.

The favored legislative mechanism for guaranteeing the
availability of insurance and one of the most common types
of legislation enacted in 1975–76 (in thirty-four states and
Puerto Rico) was the creation of something called a joint
underwriting association, or JUA.[12] This is a mandated
pooling arrangement in which all companies that sell liability insurance (not necessarily including malpractice insurance) in the state are required to participate. In most
cases the JUA becomes operational when the state insurance commissioner determines that malpractice insurance is
unavailable on the commercial market on a reasonably
competitive basis; at that point the JUA may become the
exclusive source of malpractice insurance or may serve as
an alternative to other sources. If the JUA suffers losses,
assessments are made against participating insurance com-

panies to make up the deficit; under most statutes such assessments can then be recouped, either by deductions from state premium taxes or by surcharges imposed on premiums charged doctors and hospitals (known as retrospective rating). The participating insurers are thus protected against losses; they are also, however, precluded from making a profit, the JUA being a non-profit entity.

In some states, JUA's can charge lower premiums than would otherwise be the case, because their enabling legislation permits them to issue policies on what is called a claims-made basis, as opposed to the traditional occurrence basis. An occurrence policy provides coverage against liability stemming from incidents that occur during the policy year; if a surgeon has such a policy covering 1977, for example, he is insured against any claim involving surgery he performed that year, even if the claim is not asserted until, say, 1979. A claims-made policy—which can be issued by commercial insurers as well as by JUA's—provides protection only against claims asserted in the policy year, regardless of when the incident in question took place. In claims-made malpractice insurance the proviso is added that the claim must not only be filed in the policy year but must also stem from an incident occurring in either the policy year or a previous year in which the insured was covered by the same insurer. Consequently, the carrier's risk for the first year of coverage is minimal, since most claims asserted that year will stem from incidents occurring in a previous year (and presumably will be covered by the doctor's or hospital's former occurrence policy). In future years the insurer's risk is greater but is much more easily calculated than under occurrence coverage; by the end of the year the insurer can gauge what its liability for that year will be and can make realistic adjustments in the premiums for the following year. Doctors, of course, are left out on a limb when they retire or die, still vulnerable to claims stemming from previous years of practice; to alleviate this predicament, a doctor or a doctor's estate can buy something called tail coverage, the price of which is likely to be high.

To return to the JUA's: one of their distinguishing characteristics in most states was that they were temporary; most legislation providing for their creation, that is, also provided a termination date for their statutory authority, usually two or three years after enactment. The theory was that JUA's represented an extraordinary, stopgap solution to the immediate availability problem, designed only to tide things over until long-term solutions had taken effect. In the real world, that theory was equally a reflection of the insurance industry's hostility to JUA's and a means of dampening that hostility by assuring carriers that they would not be stuck with a JUA indefinitely. In the meantime, the ability of a hostile industry to perform something like sabotage of a JUA was shown in New York, where the staff of a study commission found that that state's presumably operational JUA "seems to be not much more than a mail box or telephone booth. . . . For months physicians and hospitals have had great difficulty establishing communications with it." [13]

If doctors and hospitals wanted to stay away from both the commercial insurance market (where it existed) and the jerry-built expedient of the JUA, a theoretical alternative was to form doctor-owned or hospital-owned insurance companies. During 1975–76, eleven states passed legislation that authorized the formation of health-care mutual insurance companies, and many other states had existing insurance laws on the books that made possible the creation of such captive insurers.[14] (A captive insurer is one wholly owned by one business or a closed group; i.e., the carrier and its customers are identical.) The commercial liability insurers looked on the prospect of such do-it-yourself carriers with some ambivalence. They were glad to get rid of a troublesome line of business but were worried that they would suffer if a health-care mutual became insolvent; this because forty-eight states have insolvency laws that in such an event would require all liability insurers to contribute to an insolvency guaranty fund to pay off valid claims against the insolvent insurer.[15]

Another scheme to alleviate the insurance crunch, sometimes enacted as an alternative to a JUA, usually in addition to it, was the creation of a patients' compensation fund, which was effected by legislation in fourteen states and Puerto Rico.[16] This is a government-run entity that is responsible for paying that portion of malpractice judgments or settlements above a designated amount, usually $100,000, thereby setting a limit on the loss per claim that must be borne by insurance. Since the funds are generally financed by charges imposed on doctors and hospitals, however, the intended beneficiaries would ultimately be hurt in the aggregate if the funds suffered losses. (In some states provision for a patients' compensation fund was combined with establishment of an absolute ceiling on the amount a person can recover for a malpractice claim; such limitations are discussed next.)

These various mechanisms for making insurance available were something like a shot of morphine, wiping out the immediate agony for a limited period without affecting the underlying situation, which might or might not improve in the meantime. The underlying insurance situation was the narrow base of insureds on which to spread the risk and the unpredictability of what the quantum of risk—how many claims and in what amounts—would turn out to be.

Bringing under control at least the amounts of damages being recovered was the aim of one straightforward legislative approach, represented by a group of statutes (enacted during this period in eleven states and the Virgin Islands) that established a limit on the amount of damages a victim of malpractice could recover.[17] There were two variations on this strategy, the most common creating an absolute limit on recovery, ranging from $150,000 to $750,000, the other establishing a limit only on the amount of damages recoverable for non-economic losses (usually known as pain and suffering).

Even before they were enacted, the recovery limitations were being branded by the malpractice bar as unconstitutional because they discriminated against malpractice plaintiffs in relation to other litigants and/or because they deprived such plaintiffs of a preexisting common-law right without granting them any compensating benefit. The Illinois Supreme Court agreed with those arguments, ruling in May 1976 that that state's $500,000 limitation on malpractice recoveries violated the state constitution.[18] Litigation was meanwhile bouncing around the courts in at least three other states,[19] and one respected medicolegal authority was predicting that none of the limitation laws would survive constitutional attack.[20]

Setting aside considerations of constitutionality or equity, the problem with this class of legislation was that its effect was so minimal as to make it hard to take seriously. Although it is true that in one state the limitation imposed for a single injury or death was only $150,000, the eleven other statutes in this category created limitations of at least $500,000. According to a study by the National Association of Insurance Commissioners of over 24,000 malpractice claims closed during the year ending June 30, 1976, those in which $500,000 or more was paid out represented less than 1 percent of the claims and 6 percent of the total indemnity paid.[21] In some states the limitation established was higher than any payout that had ever been made in that state to any malpractice claimant.[22] The limitation laws, then, seemed to represent more a case of image-mongering—multimillion-dollar malpractice recoveries being pictured as an ominous threat to the fragile stucture of American medical practice—than of anything resembling reasoned cost-effectiveness analysis. A more calculating approach would have shown that as limitations become low enough to be cost-effective, their inherent unfairness becomes too blatant for them to be politically palatable, however impressive the medical lobby may be.

A more subtle strategy for reducing malpractice awards (adopted during 1975–76 in sixteen states and the Virgin Islands) was to eliminate or modify a long-established, widely accepted common-law principle known as the collateral source rule.[23] This provides that in calculating damages (representing medical expenses, lost earnings, and so on) any benefits a plaintiff may have received from collateral sources (such as health insurance, sick pay, workers' compensation) may not be considered. The theory of the rule has been that a wrongdoer should not be rewarded for the prudence of the victim in taking out insurance, a theory that becomes less than compelling when damages are usually paid out of liability insurance and when the health insurance and other benefits accruing to the patient are usually an automatic concomitant of employment or a government benefit. Thus, the double recovery available to successful plaintiffs who have other sources of compensation for their injuries was an attractive target for legislative incision.

A relatively conservative approach to doing something about the collateral source rule (taken in seven states, including the malpractice litigation centers of California and New York) was to permit the jury to hear evidence of the plaintiff's compensation from collateral sources and to do what it would with that information. A more straightforward approach was taken by another group of statutes, which provided that the jury's award, determined without reference to collateral sources, would simply be reduced by the amount the plaintiff had received from such sources.

While as a matter of fairness it was hard to defend the sanctity of the collateral source rule, it was by the same token hard to avoid the unfairness of sanctioning lesser recoveries to persons suing doctors and hospitals than to similarly injured persons suing, say, drivers or corporations; a lower court in Ohio, in fact, found this inequity sufficient reason to declare unconstitutional that state's modification of the collateral source rule.[24] And it was difficult to predict how effective eliminating or modifying the rule would actually be in reducing malpractice payouts, especially in those states where juries were free to minimize or disregard evidence of collateral payments. One analysis estimated that where the rule was eliminated altogether, malpractice award dollars would be reduced by about 20 percent, but hastened to add that insurance carriers were loath to lower premiums without some years of actual experience.[25]

A final item in the general category of financial housekeeping was doing something to regulate the medical lobby's favorite bugaboo, the trial lawyer's contingent fee. Seventeen states and the Virgin Islands adopted some sort of limitation on contingent fees in malpractice cases (two additional states had already done so by court rule), either by empowering the courts to decide the reasonableness of attorneys' fees, establishing a flat percentage of recovery as the attorney's fee, or setting forth a sliding scale under which successively higher recoveries brought successively lower percentages to the lawyer.[26] Like the changes made in the collateral source rule, this class of legislation would have made infinitely more sense had it extended to litigation generally; the myopia of the medical lobby in seeing a problem only in the case of malpractice litigation left it vulnerable to charges of unfairness and possibly of unconstitutionality. On the other hand, it was hard to see how precluding a lawyer's windfall from the occasional blockbuster award would translate into fewer claims, or lower costs, of any magnitude worth noticing.

But if delusion seemed to overshadow reality in the area of litigation finances, it devoured reality altogether in the area of what the medical lobby was fond of calling tort reform. Here it is probably safe to generalize that organized medicine's ability to win what it touted as enormous legislative victories reflected in fact the relative unimportance of the issues (as the legal lobby well knew) in terms of concrete results.

Among the favorite targets of the doctors' animosity toward the common law of malpractice were the two doctrines known as *res ipsa loquitur* and informed consent. The former doctrine was created when a nineteenth-century English judge decided it would be more judge-like to couch in Latin what in English would have been the observation that the thing speaks for itself.[27] The thing in that case was the fact that a man innocently walking by the warehouse of a dealer in flour had been struck by a barrel of flour falling from a window; the judge was disagreeing with the contention of the flour dealer's lawyer that the injured passerby could only recover damages for his injuries if he could present direct evidence that the barrel had fallen as a result of someone's negligence. The court found it just to allow the case to proceed on the common-sense assumption that barrels, when they are carefully handled, don't fall on innocent passersby, leaving the defendant free to present evidence that in his case this common-sense assumption was unjustified. The classic analogy to the falling barrel in the medical setting is the surgical instrument discovered postoperatively in the patient's gut, in which event the patient is hardly in a position to present an eyewitness account of how it got there and it seems reasonable to assume that someone's carelessness was the cause. In such a case, the doctrine spares the plaintiff from either having to prove directly what happened in the operating room or from having to produce an expert witness to testify that leaving an instrument in the patient is not in accordance with generally accepted surgical practice.

The precise nuances, embellishments, and rules of applicability surrounding *res ipsa* have differed among various jurisdictions, but doctors in all localities have convinced themselves—possibly because *res ipsa* introduces lay common sense into the area claimed by their expertise—that the doctrine represents an intolerable threat. In twelve states, during 1975–76, they won passage of legislation saying something about the doctrine, although in many cases that something turned out to be simply a codification of existing case law as to situations in which *res ipsa* was applicable or as to its effect as a rebuttable presumption.[28] At worst, the impact of the new legislation on individual cases would probably be to require expert testimony to establish propositions that could formerly be established without it.

Closely akin to *res ipsa loquitur* in the demonology of the medical profession has been the doctrine of informed consent, an elaboration of the notion that an individual has a right to protect his body against invasions to which he has not consented. In the medical setting, that notion acknowledges that consent, to be worthy of the name, must be based on knowledge of what one is consenting to; more specifically, what risks one is undergoing for the sake of what potential benefits. The doctrine of informed consent allows a patient to recover damages even if the doctor performed his medical maneuvers without negligence if one of the known risks of the particular treatment came to pass and if the patient can establish that he would not have consented to treatment had the doctor informed him of that risk. Some litigation and considerable comment has been generated around the question of the precise scope of a doctor's obligation to disclose the risks of treatment. In practice the doctrine has usually been invoked as an embellishment to a claim of negligent treatment, a lawyer's hedge against the possibility that negligence will be difficult to prove.

Perhaps because the doctrine grants the patient an important role in the decision-making process, informed consent has evoked enormous hostility from members of the medical profession. That hostility was translated into new statutes, enacted in twenty-two states, codifying informed consent or limiting its applicability. Many states created a presumption of valid consent if the consent was obtained in writing on a form meeting specified criteria, which in some instances were more detailed than existing case law; in Ohio the statute went so far as to include a suggested consent form, complete with alternatives to check off and blanks to fill in.[29] That the hullabaloo was rather far removed from the real world of malpractice claims is suggested by a statistic from the National Association of Insurance Commissioners study, which found that claims in which informed consent was raised as an issue—not necessarily the only issue or the most important issue—accounted for 2 percent of the total indemnity paid out.[30]

An even more popular subject of legislation was something even more ephemeral, except in the medical psyche— the *ad damnum* clause. This is not a piece of legalistic swearing but the punch line of the complaint that initiates a lawsuit, in which the plaintiff asks to be awarded a specified sum in damages. While observers of the legal scene have always known that the relation of the *ad damnum* clause to damages actually received was roughly comparable to the relation of the initial asking price in a Turkish bazaar to the price a knowledgeable customer could bargain for, doctors have found it disquieting to read in the papers of colleagues being sued for amounts in six or seven figures and have complained that the *ad damnum* clause supplies the press with an opportunity to give the profession a bad name. Legislatures in no fewer than twenty-seven states were persuaded to enact legislation on the issue during 1975–76, in almost all cases eliminating the *ad damnum* clause altogether.[31] Although trial lawyers may miss not being able to boast of how many doctors they are suing for a million dollars, they have always had to present concrete evidence of monetary damages before they could gain any amount for their clients, whether by jury award or settlement. It is therefore hard to see how this class of legislation could reduce the amounts being paid out to malpractice plaintiffs, much less affect the number of suits being filed.

The most popular type of enactment paraded as tort reform involved not an obscure Latinized doctrine but the straightforward concept of a deadline for suing, the statute of limitations; legislation tightening up the statute of limitations in malpractice cases passed the legislatures of thirty-five states, Puerto Rico, and the Virgin Islands.[32] In addition to a simple shortening of the basic period within which suit must be brought, the legislation usually limited the effect of judge-made exceptions to it, notably one called the discovery rule, under which the limitation period for the archetypal surgical patient with a sponge in his internal anatomy, for example, is computed from the patient's discovery of that fact, rather than from the original operation. Typically, the new laws recognized such exceptions to a limited extent but made them subject to an absolute maximum time period from the date of the incident that was the basis of the claim. Several states also modified the classical feature of statutes of limitations that, in cases involving minors, the counting process does not start until the age of majority; usually the new statutes provided a cutoff age, such as six or eight, beyond which the general time limitation would be applied.

The justification for shortening the statute of limitations was usually couched in terms of reducing the long tail of malpractice litigation and its insidious effect on insurance pricing; for that purpose, however, the increasingly common switch to claims-made insurance was a much more effective remedy. Another justification, usually unspoken, was the aim of reducing the number of lawsuits being filed. Some trial lawyers argued, however, that the effect would simply be that suits would be filed more quickly;[33] another possibility was that some claims that could have been resolved short of litigation would become lawsuits simply because the statute of limitations was about to expire. Even without such changes in lawyers' behavior, the effect of the new laws—which typically allowed a two-year or three-year period plus some exceptions—was not likely to be dramatic. The National Association of Insurance Commissioners study found that 84 percent of claims (representing 76 percent of indemnity paid) were reported within two years of the incident and that 94 percent (representing 89 percent of indemnity) were reported within three years.[34] Some percentage of those not reported would qualify even under the new laws for an exception to the general limitation.

However relatively ineffective in the real world the grab bag of measures touted as malpractice reform was destined to be, one symbolic effect was to set apart doctors (and, to a lesser extent, hospitals) as a privileged class of defendants receiving preferential treatment at the hands of the legal system. Aside from the question of constitutionality or the question of fairness to other targets of litigation such a distinction raises, it is questionable whether reinforcing the image of the medical profession as a privileged class was ultimately a sensible step for the medical lobby to take, given the public resentment of just that status.

But changing the rules governing how much and under what circumstances a victim of malpractice could recover wasn't all the legislatures, spurred on by the doctors, were up to during 1975 and 1976; they also engaged in some tinkering with the process by which claims of malpractice are resolved. Such tinkering tended to deal with two specific mechanisms, pretrial screening panels and arbitration.

Pretrial screening panels (which were legislated about in twenty-four states, Puerto Rico, and the Virgin Islands) represent a detour on the way to the jury, usually mandatory and usually taken before a suit is filed, that is intended to encourage settlement or else to reduce the power of the jury by injecting the views of an expert body into the trial process.[35] The composition of the screening panels varies widely but usually includes one or more doctors, lawyers, and members who are neither. Hearings are private and are intended to be less formal than trials, and the rules of evidence are somewhat relaxed. In no state are the findings of pretrial panels binding on the parties in the sense of cutting off their right to go ahead and litigate; in most states, however, the panel's findings are admissible in evidence at a subsequent trial, and in some states court costs are assessed against a party who goes to trial and loses in the face of adverse findings by a panel.

There is some fragmentary evidence that pretrial panels induce settlement of cases that probably would have gone to trial, although many of those would have been settled at the jury-selection stage.[36] On the other hand, as the staff of one study commission noted, "The malpractice problem and the crisis of 1975 were not the result of court congestion." [37] In terms of the insurance crisis, the value of the panels would have to be in reducing the payouts and other costs of claims (they obviously don't reduce the number of claims); the experience in New York, however, where such panels existed by court rule before they were mandated by law, was that "growth in the size of settlements coming out of mediation panels has been as dramatic as the general rise in claims cost, if not more so." [38] Thus, savings would appear to be limited to the relatively trivial reduction in legal costs resulting from the fact that a panel's hearing is shorter than a trial.

Among dispute-resolving mechanisms, arbitration is in two respects a more drastic departure from the norm than a screening procedure—it is both binding on the parties and a complete substitute for litigation. (The word "arbitration" is sometimes used to describe non-binding pretrial procedures, but knowledgeable commentators universally agree that it is properly limited to a process that is binding and final.) During the 1975–76 wave of malpractice legislation, ten states, including some with laws requiring malpractice screening panels, passed statutes explicitly providing for voluntary arbitration of malpractice claims; an eleventh state joined the ranks early in 1977. Ignoring the common opinion that it would be unconstitutional to compel parties in a malpractice dispute to arbitrate rather than litigate, Puerto Rico enacted a mandatory malpractice arbitration law. In thirty-six states voluntary arbitration as an alternative to litigation of malpractice claims was already available under general arbitration laws.[39]

The malpractice arbitration laws go into considerable, and considerably varying, detail on the many facets of an arbitration procedure: the nature of the arbitration agreement, including provisions designed to assure that the option is adequately explained to the patient and sometimes providing that the patient may cancel the agreement within a specified period after signing it; the composition and selection of the arbitration panel (or selection of a single arbitrator, which is sometimes provided for when claims are relatively small); the means by which the panel is paid (arbitration being a private mechanism, unlike litigation, the parties usually have to pay the decision-makers); the panel's method of operation; and the form and content of the arbitration award (as the panel's decision is called).[40] The substantive standards governing a doctor's or hospital's liability to a patient are the same for purposes of arbitration as they are for purposes of litigation, including the assorted modifications in tort law enacted along with the new arbitration statutes.

Doctors have generally liked the idea of arbitration as a replacement for litigation, a sentiment that reflects in part their contempt for lay juries, in part their preference for a process that is closed to the public, and in part their belief that arbitration awards would be lower than jury verdicts.[41] The dearth of experience in malpractice arbitration makes it impossible to definitively judge how realistic such preconceptions are; it is interesting to note, however, that the executive director of the Suffolk County (New York) Medical Society reported to a conference on malpractice arbitration that the experience of its arbitration program had been that "physician members of the arbitration panel tended to favor higher awards and ruled more often for negligence than the lawyer members of the panel." [42] (The privacy of the arbitration process, as it shields the defendant-doctor from public attack, may simultaneously make it easier for the arbitrator-doctor to find fault with another member of the profession.) Keeping in mind that, of the minuscule proportion of malpractice claims that become trials (about 4 percent), doctors win about 80 percent,[43] it is also interesting to note that, of three studies of cases that went through the full arbitration process, patients were awarded damages in 45 percent, 47 percent, and 70 percent of the cases.[44] (Of claims that start the arbitration route, something between a half and two-thirds are settled before the adjudication stage.[45]) Thus, the psychological benefit of the private aspect of arbitration may not be accompanied by an economic benefit to the medical profession.

Arguments that arbitration offers superior speed and lower administrative costs than litigation were made and disputed,[46] but it was impossible to settle such arguments definitively before several years of widespread experience had been accumulated. In the meantime, it seemed safe to conclude that whatever the marginal advantages of the arbitration process to both sides, its adoption was incapable of having any significant effect on the malpractice problem in terms of reducing the numbers of claims or the amounts of payouts. More generally, the cost-effectiveness of expending so much energy to establish new mechanisms of dispute resolution was rather dubious, considering that something over 90 percent of malpractice claims were being settled before trial or abandoned.[47] Such settlements might be accelerated by the new procedures, but the price in administrative energy spent learning about and adjusting to them seemed disproportionate to that benefit.

While the legislatures were going on their 1975–76 binge of malpractice enactments, some discussion was taking place, mostly in academic circles and among the staff members of study commissions, of junking altogether both the process and the substantive basis of malpractice compensation and adopting something loosely called a no-fault system of compensating people with medical injuries. What kept such a notion at the level of theoretical speculation was the unavoidable problem that determining whether a given situation would constitute what the experts call a compensable event under a no-fault system would be no easier than determining whether a given situation constitutes medical negligence under the fault system. The attempted analogy to no-fault auto insurance, in other words, broke down when it became painfully clear that establishing that someone suffered a broken leg as a result of an anto accident is infinitely simpler than establishing that someone's less-than-optimal recovery from surgery was a result of the surgery as opposed to the person's preexisting condition.

Not even academics, however, were discussing the possibility of taking the logical next step and leaving the entire morass behind by creating a single system of compensation for victims of medical mishaps and all others placed in a comparable position. The argument would be that, if a person needs an operation, whether because a surgeon botched a previous operation, because a drunken driver smashed his car and him in it, because he fell over his niece's tricycle, or because he developed acute appendicitis, there should be one system, rather than four, for financing his medical treatment. The argument would be the same for a person who needed permanent nursing care or housekeeping assistance because he was paralyzed, whether the paralysis resulted from a surgical error, an auto accident, or a stroke. The difficulty with such a line of argument—and undoubtedly the reason that it wasn't being aired—is that it implies a re-examination and overhaul of the jerry-built, inequity-ridden structure of financing medical treatment, compensating the disabled, and otherwise dealing with society's less-than-fully-productive members.

Such an approach would of course require addressing separately the need for some kind of accountability in medical practice, a function the tort system of compensating medical injuries pretends to perform. Possibly in recognition of the tort system's inadequacies in this connection, more likely because they felt the need to protect their credibility as more than an arm of the state medical society, legislatures in thirty-eight states and the Virgin Islands enacted statutes aimed at strengthening in some way the process of physician discipline. These measures typically involved broadening the sanctions available to the state licensing and discipline board beyond simple revocation of the offending doctor's license; broadening the grounds for which sanctions could be invoked against a physician (which in many states had previously not included medical incompetence); granting immunity from suit to those who provide information to licensing and discipline boards; and requiring some form of continuing medical education.[48]

A related class of legislation, enacted in thirty-one states, required the reporting to some state agency of all malpractice claims, settlements, and judgments;[49] a few states also required such bodies as medical societies and hospital committees to report complaints or actions reflecting physician incompetence. While these data-reporting provisions were largely motivated by the discovery the malpractice crisis brought that existing data about malpractice claims and their disposition were fragmentary and less than totally reliable, they were also meant to provide bodies charged with physician discipline with a new source of information.

It is not clear whether the new legislation on physician discipline was being accompanied by increased appropriations for the state agencies being charged with an expanded range of functions. The problem is illustrated by a January 1977 report of the New York State Consumer Protection Board, which found that that state's new Board for Professional Medical Conduct was struggling to handle a backlog of 551 cases with a staff of twelve investigators. Its task was not made easier by the fact that due process for complained-against physicians under the new legislation was deemed to require that the imposition of sanctions be preceded by no fewer than nine stages in the administrative process, plus two levels of court review.[50]

There is also the problem that no structure of medical discipline, however streamlined or well-funded, could operate effectively without leads to follow and that the most reliable leads to physician incompetence necessarily come from other health professionals. Legislative bodies found themselves incapable, however, of outlawing the code of loyalty that creates a we-versus-them mentality among such professionals. Another investigative report on the new New York legislation, for example, found that very few reports of professional misconduct were coming from professionals or county medical societies; what was worse, a new state regulation requiring that hospitals report denials or withdrawals of physician privileges based on professional conduct was being evaded by the common expedient of requesting physicians to resign before their privileges were cut off.[51] Even requirements that certain malpractice judgments and settlements be reported to some state agency were creating a distortion of the usual settlement process, as reflected in the following tidbit appearing in a medical magazine: "A recent malpractice case that could have been settled for $45,000 went to trial in Los Angeles when the three doctors and one hospital involved would offer no more than $40,000. The jury awarded the plaintiff $344,443. The settlement failed mainly because no doctor wanted to pay as much as $3,000, which would necessitate a report to the state Board of Medical Quality Assurance." [52]

More fundamentally, of course, the problem with such administrative structures is that at best they are limited to shooting down bad apples. The surgeon whose technique in the operating room is superb but who treats his patients like mildly interesting specimens of pathology whose anxieties and life problems have nothing to do with him has nothing to fear from a medical discipline board, even one operating under the best of circumstances. He will, however, have patients who are dissatisfied, even angry, with his treatment of them, and sooner or later his superb technique will not spare him from being sued for malpractice by one (or more) of them.

But if the state legislatures were by their nature unequipped to deal with such subtleties, doctors and hospitals were too busy becoming insurance experts to be bothered. Spurred on by the dismal state of the marketplace and the newly enacted enabling legislation, a number of medical societies and hospital associations were making do-it-yourself insurance a major new activity. By early 1977 something like thirteen state medical societies had set up captive malpractice insurance carriers (irreverently known as bedpan mutuals),[53] as had twenty-one groupings of hospitals, thirteen of them state hospital associations.[54] Both the American Medical Association and the American Hospital Association had created national captives to provide reinsurance to their local counterparts.[55] Perhaps the most impressive captive insurer was a venture called Controlled Risk Insurance Company, Ltd. (CRICO), established early in 1976 on the British Crown Colony of Grand Cayman Island in the Caribbean for the purpose of providing $50 million worth of claims-made insurance coverage to each of twelve hospitals and their three thousand physicians affiliated with Harvard University. The advantage of the exotic location was that its government imposed no corporate tax or income tax, a fact that was projected to translate into $4 million worth of savings for 1976.[56] The Massachusetts insurance commissioner, for his part, was said to have observed that CRICO had been established without his approval and in violation of the "spirit" of Massachusetts law.[57]

The Minnesota insurance commissioner was reported early in 1977 to have driven his state's hospital association offshore. The Minnesota Hospital Association announced plans to establish a captive in Bermuda, complaining that the insurance commissioner had refused to support legislation permitting establishment of captive insurers with fewer than three hundred participants and that it was futile to try to pass insurance legislation without the commissioner's endorsement.[58] While other state hospital associations and the state medical associations were keeping their captives domestic, six other groups of hospitals had based their insurance mutuals in Bermuda.[59] The Bermudan government was not permitting the creation of captive insurance companies that covered only individuals, but a number of ad hoc groups of doctors, usually of a single specialty or malpractice-risk category, and sometimes numbering only twenty-five or so, were reported establishing captives on Grand Cayman Island.[60]

The operation of the captives was apparently not without its problems, whatever the smugness of the professionals in having freed themselves of the insurance companies. Most of the doctor mutuals were selling only limited coverage ($100,000 per occurrence, $300,000 per year) because they lacked the capital to offer more, and they usually sold it on a claims-made basis.[61] In the event of a few catastrophic losses, their doctor-owners faced the prospect of having to cough up special assessments on top of their premiums.[62] Most hospital captives were encountering difficulties in buying reinsurance and in contracting out for services like

claims handling.[63] It was doubtful whether in the long run
the new enterprises would be able to stay afloat.

A new activity closely allied with the insurance goings-on
at the hospital level was something called risk management,
a concept previously limited to more industrial spheres.
(The Pennsylvania Hospital Association's captive insurance
company was reported to be running a risk-management
program modeled after "Defense Department methods for
reducing the possibility of errors in U.S. missile and space
programs." [64]) Both the American Hospital Association and
the Federation of American Hospitals published manuals
on the subject,[65] several state hospital associations claimed
to be running or planning risk-management programs,
something called the Hospital Association of Risk Managers came into being, and a number of private risk-
management consultants started selling their services to hospital administrations.[66] The Florida legislature even passed
a statute requiring hospitals to establish risk-management
committees, although a lower court early in 1977 found the
law to be constitutionally defective in assorted respects.[67]

The flurry of activity concealed a fundamental problem
with the risk-management approach. While such programs
may improve the monitoring of equipment for hidden defects or increase the accuracy of a medication-distribution
system, their design is such that they have very little effect
on the conduct of physicians, although physician conduct
is at the root of both the majority of malpractice claims and
the most expensive malpractice claims. This limitation stems
from a reluctance by hospital administrators to tread very
heavily on the toes of their medical staffs, a reluctance that
is rational in terms of the administrators' need to maintain
the good will of those who keep their beds filled but that is
not rational in terms of effectively minimizing the risk of
malpractice claims.[68]

The net effect of an enormous expenditure of energy on
the malpractice issue by legislators and professionals was to

keep under control for the time being the most superficial aspect of the problem, the crisis in insurance availability and affordability. A malpractice roundup published in early 1977 reported that physicians were finding basic insurance coverage available in all states (so-called umbrella coverage, for the outsized awards, was hard to get in several states), although in five states the only insurance source was a JUA and in eight others the only source was a doctor-owned mutual. Insurance prices were said to be rising no more rapidly than medical prices generally, a fact that was in part attributable to the switch to claims-made insurance by one of the major commercial carriers (St. Paul) and by many of the JUA's and health-care mutuals.[69] Considering the temporary nature of most JUA's, the fragile foundations of the health-care mutuals, the fact that claims-made insurance has to get more expensive after the first year of coverage, and, finally, the likelihood that the much-touted malpractice reform laws would not effect significant reductions in the number and size of claims, the structure of what called itself malpractice reform turned out to be as unstable as the proverbial house of cards. And the proclamations of the end of crisis—to anyone who closely examined their underlying premises—turned out to be as far removed from reality as the rhetoric of the malpractice debate had been. It was hard to say precisely when or precisely where the malpractice crisis would undergo a reincarnation, but that it would in some form reemerge was inescapable.

But even assuming that the insurance crisis had been disposed of definitively, there remained virtually untouched at least two fundamental dimensions of the malpractice problem. There were first the inequities of differential compensation of victims of medical mishaps: the fact that some do and some do not get compensated for their injuries; that of those who do, some are undercompensated and some overcompensated; and that in all events the compensation system is cumbersome, unpredictable, and imposes enormous practical and psychological burdens on the unhappy patient. More important, there were the risks and frustrations of modern medical practice, with the inevitable by-product of some patients who suffer injuries and some injured patients who are angered by that fact; at this level, the increasingly defensive maneuvers of doctors in practice, combined with the successful assertion of special privilege by the medical lobby, seemed destined, if anything, only to increase the likelihood of patients feeling resentful enough to take to the courts.

I2

The Dilemmas of Reform

Any instrument of liberation can also be used for domination.
JOEL KOVEL, M.D., *A Complete Guide to Therapy*

*It is, of course, in the very nature of a myth that those who
are its victims and, at the same time, its perpetrators, should,
by virtue of these two facts, be rendered unable to examine the
myth, or even suspect, much less recognize, that it is a myth
which controls and blasts their lives.*
JAMES BALDWIN, *Nothing Personal*

THE malpractice debate inspired by the 1975 insurance
crisis included very little advocacy on behalf of the interests of patients—except as those interests were appropri-
ated by the malpractice bar for its own ulterior purposes—
probably because most established activities involving patient advocacy tended to focus, not on the character of medical treatment, but on broad issues of access to, and organization of, services and issues of quality in its most generic
sense. This does not mean that dissatisfaction with medical
treatment (of which a malpractice suit is the most extreme
expression) has not provoked organized activity by those
on the receiving end. The 1970's have seen the development
of three such movements—distinguishable, albeit overlap-
ping—which can be identified as medical consumerism,
medical self-care, and medical self-help. Each has sprung
from particular evident needs, and each offers something by
way of immediate response to such needs. Each, however,
subscribes in the end to at least the core assumptions of the
biomedical model, accepting and even conspiring with the
grounding of modern medical practice in an economistic,
overtechnologized, overbureaucratized base, rather than an

[169]

ethical, humanistic base consonant with the human experience of sickness.

Medical consumerism was the only one of the three movements that made itself heard on the malpractice issue with any regularity. The representative of consumerism in most instances was the Health Research Group, one of the Public Citizen groups that make up the Ralph Nader conglomerate, and probably the most conspicuous and influential manifestation of medical consumerism in general. (HRG's range of concerns has also included occupational, environmental, and nutritional safety, as well as consumer participation in health planning, all of which will for present purposes be ignored.) The nature of the critique of medical practice put forth by medical consumerism can be seen in a statement on the malpractice crisis by HRG's director, Sidney M. Wolfe, M.D. After observing that the malpractice phenomenon is "but one of many evidences of the public dissatisfaction with the health care system," Wolfe points to "poor technical quality" and "the deteriorating doctor-patient relationship" as the sources of that dissatisfaction. The problem of the doctor-patient relationship is then seen as a problem of information, or rather, the lack of it—"the state of ignorance which the medical profession has imposed for centuries and continues to impose on the public." [1] Thus, the logical thrust of medical consumerist activities is to provide the public with information, both to enable it to avoid poor technical quality in medical treatment and to fill the information gaps that are left by practitioners, however well qualified.

Perhaps the originator of the current literature of medical consumerism was a public official who became something of a consumerist folk hero, then Pennsylvania Insurance Commissioner Herbert Denenberg, who in the early 1970's issued (or used his powers of persuasion to induce Blue Cross plans to issue) a series of what he called shopper's guides, which in the health field concerned themselves with dentists, hospitals, surgery, and health insurance. His *Shopper's Guide to Surgery,* for example, sets forth fourteen rules described as enabling the reader to avoid unnecessary surgery, although some of them (making sure that the surgeon is board-certified and a fellow of the American College of Surgeons, for example) appear more concerned with the quality of the surgery than with the question of its necessity. The preface explains that the broader purpose of the guide is to "make our free enterprise system of competition work like it's supposed to." [2]

The Health Research Group has taken the shopper's guide approach to the extent of issuing a guide on X rays,[3] but its most significant information-producing activity has been in the area of doctors' directories. These list the credentials, office hours, fees, hospital affiliations, and policy on making house calls and taking Medicaid and Medicare patients of medical practitioners in a given area. The first such directory, issued in January 1974, concerned doctors in Prince Georges County, Maryland (a suburb of Washington); over the next two years at least thirty directories were reported to have been published in fifteen states.[4]

This informational activity was not without its obstacles; only about 25 percent of the Prince Georges County physicians agreed to be listed in the HRG directory, the rest hiding behind the fact that state law as well as medical ethics prohibited advertising by physicians. The same day it issued the Prince Georges County directory, the HRG filed a suit challenging the Maryland law, and similar litigation followed in Virginia and New York. A three-judge court in Virginia ruled late in 1976 that a statute prohibiting doctors from providing information on fees and services for a consumer directory was unconstitutional because it contravened the First Amendment.[5]

In the meantime, the American Medical Association had shifted its position on physician advertising, its Judicial Council deciding in May 1976 that medical ethics would not be violated if a doctor provided information, including standard fees, to a "reputable" directory. (The HRG pronounced itself "encouraged that the AMA has taken the lead over other professional organizations . . . in accepting the principle that the public is 'entitled to know' about the details of a physician's practice." [6]) At about the same time, a survey conducted by *Medical Economics* found that 60 percent of its sample were willing to list themselves in a consumer directory, although when asked about making public their fees (without regard to the medium), 82 percent were opposed.[7] By mid-1977 the Prince Georges County Medical Society had decided to do the HRG one better by publishing its own directory, a medical society in suburban Denver and a doctors' union in Arizona had already published directories, and an AMA official was quoted as saying, "We think directories are a good idea; they're great PR." [8]

The reformist rationale for the doctors' directories is identical to the rationale for evaluating cars and washing machines in a publication like *Consumer Reports*. In the words of one medical consumerist, with a directory "a consumer can make a reasoned choice [of doctor] without pressure in his own home," and conversely, the information provided by directories is essential "if consumers are to have the slightest chance of protecting themselves from both physical and financial harm in the medical market place." [9]

Another focus of medical consumerist concern has had to do not with gathering and promulgating information but with gaining access to a special body of information, the contents of a patient's own medical (especially hospital) record. The legalities of the issue of access to one's own medical record have been murky (and widely variable from state to state) and the practicalities often at variance with the legalities.[10] Expressions of concern about the issue have been too scattered to summarize,[11] but it is easy to summarize the consumerist rationale, thanks to a much-talked-about proposal set forth in a prestigious medical journal in 1973, in an article by Budd N. Shenkin, M.D., and David C. Warner, Ph.D.[12] The Shenkin-Warner proposal was that legislation be enacted requiring both doctors and hospitals to furnish complete, unexpurgated copies of all medical records to patients as soon as the services in question were recorded. The analogy to consumerism in the area of commercial products was made explicit: "The record to a large extent embodies the informational product of medical consultation and treatment. In most exchanges in society a purchased product becomes the property of the purchaser. . . . Patients, physicians and planners and administrators would all benefit if the conditions of open information and freedom of choice that prevail in the market were to be introduced into the area of medical care." [13]

That kind of logic on the part of medical consumerists was adopted by the federal consumer-protection bureaucracy in December 1975, when the Federal Trade Commission filed a complaint against the American Medical Association, the state medical society in Connecticut, and the county medical society in New Haven, charging restraint of competition in violation of federal antitrust legislation by virtue of organized medicine's restrictions on physician advertising and soliciting, which restrictions were said to deprive consumers of the benefits of competition, including "information pertinent to the selection of a physician." The shift in the AMA's position on doctors' directories mentioned earlier was a direct result of the FTC action; the same policy statement indicated that physicians were free to make public basic information about their practice in "accepted local media of advertising or communication"; soliciting, however, was distinguished from advertising and still found to violate medical ethics, a position that left the AMA and the FTC at odds.[14]

The FTC chairman, in a speech given in mid-1977 to an FTC-sponsored conference on "Competition in the Health

Care Sector," was almost apologetic that his agency had failed to realize earlier that medical treatment was just like dishwashers or toothpaste: "We recognize, along with most Americans, that the delivery of health care is business. . . . The Commission—like most other agencies of government —was slow to admit that one possible way to control the seemingly uncontrollable health sector could be to treat it as a business and make it respond to the same marketplace influences as other American businesses and industries." [15]

Of course medical treatment is like a dishwasher in the sense that obtaining either can turn out to be a mistake in certain instances. It must be admitted, then, that to the extent that medical consumerism is motivated by a concern about the undeniable existence of medical abuses, it is grounded in an immediate reality. To the extent that it is elevated to a long-range strategy buttressed by a theory of the medical marketplace, however, consumerism ratifies, even encourages, some of the most invidious trends in modern medical practice. The most obvious such effect is its willing acceptance of the preexisting trend to increasingly commodify the process of giving and receiving medical care. The advocates of doctors' directories, for example, when they disparage (as they commonly do) the typical practice of choosing a doctor by asking one's friends and relatives if they are happy with theirs, are denying the very real healing value of doctor-patient rapport. When they encourage patients to look to academic and professional credentials in choosing a doctor, they are denying that a healer is any different from a technician (or a refrigerator).

By bringing caveat emptor to the arena of medical practice, the consumerists, consciously or otherwise, are encouraging doctors to act just like entrepreneurs, unencumbered by any social obligation to exercise ethical restraints over what they do to patients or whom they let do what to patients. Despite their pretensions to being liberal reformers, the consumerists' individualistic, every-man-for-himself economic model allies them with a view of economic reality that all but the most conservative economists have long since discarded. Milton Friedman, the dean of the economic right wing, agrees with medical consumerism that "doctor advertising is both appropriate and desirable. It promotes competition, spreads information, and reduces the monopolistic power of the A.M.A." [16] (To criticize the consumerists' economic conservatism is not to endorse the medical conservatism of the AMA or to argue that that organization has ever been a real force against the encroachments of commodification, despite its frequent self-righteous posturing about the doctor-patient relationship; as one commentator has noted parenthetically, "Scientific medicine . . . while paying copious lip service to the doctor-patient relationship, in actuality largely ignores it." [17]) The consumerist approach of dealing with medical treatment in terms of the (largely mythical) competitive marketplace, in other words, frees the practitioner and the medical institution from an obligation to their patients any greater than, or different from, the obligation of a retail store to its customers.

The ultimately dehumanizing effect of medical consumerism is perhaps most sharply seen in the proposal to routinely give patients a copy of their medical records. The notion is hideously pathetic, even defeatist, for the need of the patient that it is intended to meet is the frequently desperate need to know about the meaning of one's illness in human terms (less "What is it?" than "What does it mean for my life?"). But what the proposal offers the patient is a poorly organized, usually illegible agglomeration of isolated bits and pieces of data—vital signs, input and output, laboratory values, medication orders, observations on one's eating and sleeping habits—a system of recording and communicating intended to meet not the practical and psychological needs of patients but the technical needs of health professionals and administrators. (The Shenkin-Warner proposal acknowledges this problem to the extent of surmising that "published guides to medical care would soon flourish, and professional consultant services for records 'translation,' interpretation and evaluation would arise in response to consumer demand." [18] Presumably, counseling services would then arise in response to consumer demand for help in coping with the information provided by such consulting services, but the authors are silent on this point; indeed, they appear to be blissfully unaware that a patient's need to know about his sickness is any different from a traveler's need to know what gate his plane leaves from.) The proposal ratifies commodification, in other words, in that it addresses the human need for participation in a dialogue, even a relationship, by offering the patient possession of a thing—as if a person's need for human companionship were proposed to be met by a mannequin spouting a recorded message.

As it ratifies commodification, medical consumerism simultaneously ratifies the biomedical model and the bad-apple theory of what is wrong with the structure of medical practice. It accepts, that is to say, the view of the medical elite (who, it might be noted, are less and less identified with the AMA and more and more identified with academic medicine) that there is nothing wrong with modern American medicine that can't be corrected with an accredited medical education, certification by a specialty board, and ongoing review of technical competence. With the possible exception of its concern with unnecessary surgery, consumerism poses no challenge to the biomedical establishment but swallows unquestioningly its definition of the nature of sickness and the purpose of treatment.

Finally, by virtue of its individualistic premise, medical consumerism gives a new twist to the old American tradition of blaming the victim (as in the argument that the poor are poor because they're lazy and sinful). Rather than challenge the medical establishment to deal with what is problematic about modern medical practice (even in the narrow terms of the bad-apple theory), medical consumerism exhorts individual patients to develop the skills to enable them to compensate for and maneuver around it. Thus, for example, the publication of a New York group called the Consumer Commission on the Accreditation of Health Services tells its readers, in an issue on malpractice: "Above all, you must take the responsibility of questioning your doctor about your health. . . . It is your responsibility to avoid encouraging the doctor to assume an unrealistic role." [19] The Denenberg *Shopper's Guide to Surgery* admonishes its readers, in a similar vein, to "develop a good relationship with a family doctor"—as if a patient would consciously choose not to have a good relationship with a family doctor and as if a patient alone could determine the quality of his relationship with the person he is asking for professional help.

None of the above, it should go without saying, is to glorify patient ignorance; rather, it is to argue that knowledge acquired through a mutually trusting alliance with a healer, in a common struggle with the problem of illness, serves a radically different function from information acquired in isolation, as a weapon to ward off exploitation by a medical technocrat. Nor is it to advocate blind acceptance of things as they are; to the contrary, the problem with medical consumerism is precisely that it ignores the fundamental defect of things as they are.

Closely allied to medical consumerism, sometimes almost indistinguishable from it, is an amorphous but increasingly visible movement that calls itself medical self-care. (One medical magazine has surmised that self-care "just may be medicine's fastest rolling new bandwagon." [20]) Like medical consumerism, self-care is a fundamentally individualistic approach and one that concentrates on disseminating information. Perhaps its distinguishing characteristic is that it focuses less on how an individual can most effectively manipulate the structure of medical practice than on how he can avoid using it altogether. It believes, in the words of one of its proponents, that "the crux of the 'medical care crisis' may turn out to be the simple fact that we've allowed our doctors to carry more of the burden of providing us with health care than we should have. Much of the current criticism of the health care system conveniently avoids looking at our own behavior, at the points in our daily lives where we are offered clear choices between sickness and wellness." [21] The magazine *Medical Self-Care,* from which that quote is taken, offers its readers a sort of shopper's guide, in the style of *The Whole Earth Catalog,* to books whose subjects run the gamut from home medical care and evaluating medication to eating, running, and relaxing. Its originator and editor, a Yale medical student named Tom Ferguson, explained in an interview that he conceived of the magazine after being exposed to hospitalized patients suffering from what he regarded as self-inflicted illnesses—smokers with emphysema, heavy drinkers with liver disease, and so on. He saw the aim of self-care as being to transform the individual into "the first level of a total health care team where there would be appropriate skills assigned to the health consumer. He would do the work somewhere between that of a physician's assistant or a nurse and someone who knows nothing." [22]

Other proponents of self-care speak of a complex of values going beyond the function of preventive medicine and self-treatment: "Self-care is a concept with deep roots in the populist values of self-control and self-determinism. Its development surely will result in demystifying professional functions and may cause a reformulation of medicine's social charter." [23] The argument is further made that "lay dependency on the health care system *qua* system, and lay dependency in personal care transactions, are similarly destructive of human integrity, dignity, and autonomy." [24] On the other hand, coping with chronic diseases (which some self-care advocates speak of as the wave of the medical future) is sometimes argued to be the situation that self-care addresses uniquely well: "Chronic disease constitutes a clear and comprehensive model for self-care practice, an opportunity for laypersons to develop extensive self-care skills on a continuous and progressive basis." [25] And self-care is seen as an increasingly useful concept in light of rising costs and maldistributed resources: "For administrators and planners, who seek ways of economizing so that the time of physicians will be most appropriately employed for those patients whose complaints are most relevant to what professional skills can offer, the increasing use of self-care approaches is obviously attractive and worthy of serious study and consideration." [26]

A bridge between self-care and medical self-help, with some unique characteristics of its own, is the women's health movement, which combines the group approach that distinguishes self-help from self-care with the latter's emphasis on educating people about their bodies' functioning and malfunctioning. The operative unit of the movement is the gynecological self-help group (sometimes misleadingly called a self-help clinic), in which six to ten women come together regularly for several weeks to study basic anatomy and physiology, learn techniques of breast and vaginal self-examination, discuss contraceptives and common gynecological disorders, and share their problems in dealing with gynecologists.[27] The aim of gynecological self-help is not merely enlightenment but also self-fulfillment: "Self-help is women relating to ourselves in order to demystify health care, the professionals and our own bodies; it involves being able to make personal choices based on our very valid experiences and knowledge. Self-help is a positive action by which we can change our own lives and those of our sisters." [28] Its rationale is integrally tied to that of the larger women's movement: "The self-help clinic seeks to restore women's sense of autonomy over their lives, to restore their self-reliance, and lessen their dependency on all institutions which define the lives of women of all classes." [29] Although hard data are nonexistent, the constituency of gynecological self-help appears in fact to be predominantly middle-class, white, under thirty, and well educated [30]—women, in other words, who both come from a milieu where systematic knowledge is valued and are relatively free of inhibitions about exposing and touching their bodies in a group setting.

In a few instances, notably at the Feminist Women's Health Centers in California, gynecological self-help combines the activities described above with clinical medical treatment. The setting of treatment replaces the doctor-patient dyad with a group in which lay-professional distinctions are deliberately blurred; routine examinations and lab tests are carried out in, and largely by, groups of clients, with some assistance from a female physician or nurse-practitioner; the exclusivity of the physician role is maintained only when legalities require it, as in writing prescriptions.[31]

As gynecological self-help exists within the larger context of the women's movement, so generic medical self-help exists within the context of the larger (though more amorphous) self-help movement. Thus, for example, the *Self-Help Reporter* (a bimonthly newsletter of the National Self-Help Clearinghouse) combines items about medical self-help with news of self-help groups comprising homemakers, smokers, interracial couples, blind bowlers, mothers of twins, parents of gays and lesbians, and college teachers suffering from "academic staleness." [32] Unlike the attempt made by women's self-help to frontally challenge the medical profession and the structure of medical practice, however, self-help groups in the larger medical field are in many cases essentially adjuncts of the profession, some having been founded by physicians or operating as offshoots of established disease organizations such as the American Cancer Society.[33]

Many medical self-help groups essentially perform the function of rehabilitation in a group setting, in which people who have undergone, for example, ostomies, mastectomies, laryngectomies, or heart surgery learn to cope with their condition, sometimes by way of relatively formal instruction, more often by way of group members sharing experiences and providing emotional support to each other. The learning-to-cope function is also performed in a related but distinguishable classification of self-help groups comprising people suffering from chronic diseases such as emphysema, arthritis, and diabetes. At the edge of the medical sphere is a class of groups engaged in behavior modification of self-destructive habits, such as Alcoholics Anonymous (the oldest and one of the largest of the self-help groups), Weight Watchers, and smokEnders.[34]

Although many medical self-help groups have origins in the medical establishment, many are patient-initiated, and all aim to operate as "peer-oriented, problem-centered groups in which the participant is both the helper and the one to be helped," [35] a characteristic that is sometimes labeled "consumer intensivity." [36] Their advocates describe them as stressing "what might be called an 'aprofessional' dimension —the concrete, the subjective, the experiential, the intuitive, empathy, in contrast to the more professional accent on distance, perspective, systematic knowledge, understanding." [37] Self-help groups are sometimes contrasted with group therapy by the fact that they "neither diagnose or treat." [38] They are sometimes described in terms of providing a sick person with what the structure of medical practice fails to give him: "While the health care delivery system is not designed to provide long term friendship and support, many of these [self-help] groups focus on just such areas. The chronically ill need information and education to manage their conditions. Such information is often not readily available from their physician, but persons with similar disorders and histories are often willing to share experiences and solutions." [39] At the same time, many self-help groups remain dependent on medical professionals for referrals of potential members and access to hospitalized patients.[40]

That there is a liberating aspect to self-care and self-help activities is undeniable. Self-care and the knowledge-imparting features of self-help bring liberation from the abysmal ignorance about our bodies and how they function that is one feature of our estrangement from ourselves as physical beings. In the words of the recognized primer of women's self-help, *Our Bodies, Ourselves:* "Finding out about our bodies and our bodies' needs, starting to take control over that area of our lives, has released for us an energy that has overflowed into our work, our friendships, our relationships with men and women, and for some of us, our marriages and our parenthood." [41]

The group dynamics of a self-help group, in which participants can simultaneously break out of their isolation, receive emotional support from peers with comparable problems, and buttress their self-esteem by providing help to others, can be enormously therapeutic, as numerous accounts attest: "Women who have participated in self-help groups report feelings of strength, a sense of self-worth, self-confidence, and an ability to be more assertive." [42] "Even an outside observer of a self-help group must be impressed. The sense of community, the strength found in helping others, the determination to rise above the patient's passive role, and the energetic commitment suggest that the self-help group is the wave of the future in health care." [43] "Self-help groups and approaches offer welcome relief with respect to how we have been made to feel by taking responsibility, seeking understanding, building on a person's relatedness to others, and emphasizing individual and group competence." [44] It is not to disparage either to note that many of the positive features of self-help groups have also been found in therapy groups.[45]

Our rootlessness and isolation—the fruits of our individualistic ethos as it combines with technological change and incessant mobility—make the self-help approach immensely attractive, for both its instrumental function of providing concrete assistance and its expressive function of giving emotional support. At the same time, self-help (and to some extent self-care) combines the old American virtue of pulling oneself up by one's own bootstraps with the old American traditions of voluntarism and anti-elitism. The dangers of self-help and self-care, then, stem from the old American tradition of pragmatism, our eagerness to embrace approaches that in some sense "work," without stopping to systematically spin out the full spectrum of their consequences.

When we delight in a new-found community of mastectomees, laryngectomees, or diabetics, we neglect to notice that the self-definition that such a grouping entails has reduced our multifaceted humanity to a one-dimensional label. (The same humanity-denying reductionism is seen in the semantic act of coining a term such as "mastectomee" to describe a person who has undergone a mastectomy, a reductionism carried to its absurd extreme when the literature of self-help creates the concept of a "helpee." [46]) Rather, that is, than developing or strengthening networks of people relating to people—in families, friendship groups, or neighborhoods— we create networks that deny that our identity encompasses more than a medical category and that emphasize what is strange, even stigmatic, about us. "Self-help and mutual-aid groups by their emphasis on specific symptoms and specific problems emphasize and reinforce those problems rather than making clear that they are an integral part of total human and community life." [47]

As it falls into the trap of the medical label, self-help simultaneously falls into the trap of relieving medical practice of a range of functions that modern doctors regard as distasteful and uninteresting, rather than challenging medical practice to encompass all the human dimensions of sickness. "Members of self-help groups believe, generally as a part of feeling stigmatized, that the health care system will not meet their needs if they ask. . . . Victims of chronic diseases are generally not physicians' favorites. Surgeons do not cope well with patients they have mutilated." [48]

Rather than argue to the medical profession that the healing function goes beyond technological maneuvers, self-help simultaneously assumes an antiprofessional stance and, by itself taking on the nurturant aspect of medical care, fails to challenge medicine's narrow definition of the professional function. It thus leaves the biomedical model triumphant and its practitioners free to evade the task of integrating the social and psychological aspects of sickness with the organic symptoms of disease. Self-care, in the meantime, swallows the biomedical model to the extent of mimicking its incorrigible faddism, as in the fad for mammographies as breast-cancer detection until the light dawned that the procedure might cause as much cancer as it detected, or in the fad for reduction of cholesterol in the diet despite the distinct possibility that the theory behind that practice is simply wrong.[49]

In the end, self-help and, even more so, self-care follow medical consumerism into the trap of blaming the victim. Responsibility for health problems, that is, is located neither in the structure of medical practice nor in the physical, economic, and social environment, but is moralistically assigned to the individual. The heavy drinker or the smoker, for example, is exhorted to change his behavior without being given either effective help from the medical profession (the doctor's stern warning of impending disease and premature death is, if anything, likely to prompt him to reach for the cigarette or the bottle as a means of warding off this new anxiety) or recognition that the inhuman stresses of post-industrial society can sometimes make self-destructive habits an almost rational form of adaptation.

Their victim-blaming aspect makes self-care and self-help particularly vulnerable to cooptation by the same established powers that their anti-elitism makes them seem independent of. *The Wall Street Journal,* for example, discusses medicine in the year 2000 by quoting a miniature sermon delivered by Dr. John Knowles, the president of the Rocke-feller Foundation and long a leading figure in academic medicine: " 'The next major advance in the health of the American people will result only from what the individual is willing to do for himself.' . . . Dr. Knowles . . . asserts that many Americans have come to look on 'sloth, gluttony, alcoholic intemperance, reckless driving, sexual frenzy and smoking' as constitutional rights, and they've come to ex-pect government-financed 'cures' for all the unhappy conse-quences." [50] The Sunday *New York Times* gives space to the president emeritus of Brown University, Henry M. Wriston, so he can tell us: "Much sickness arises from failure of the will, bad judgment, lazy atrophy of the muscles." It follows that national health insurance legislation "should put a pre-mium on self-discipline. . . . Let all who, at the end of three years, can show by a complete examination that they have obeyed a few basic rules of health be given a full re-fund of all payments—*in cash*." [51] Wriston does not explain how his plan would treat those who are involuntarily ex-posed to cancer-causing substances on the job or who take to drink from inability to find a job.

Blue Cross/Blue Shield spends its subscribers' money on a newspaper-advertising campaign featuring the admonition "Don't junk your body 10 years too soon"; [52] the glossy book-let that comes to those who mail in the coupon preaches: "Remember, staying healthy is primarily your responsibility, not that of doctors and drugs." Junk food is not a curse that agribusiness casts on a consumerist society but simply a bad habit: "Don't be a 'junk food junkie.' " The automobile is not what industry has made an integral part of the Ameri-can identity but another individualistic bad habit: "Most of us need exercise. . . . It's so easy to just get out of the car and walk a bit." Overeating, it is admitted, may be a form of coping: "Let's realize that eating may be your way of responding to stress, anxiety, boredom, anger." This does not mean, however, that the sources of stress and so forth should be examined, much less challenged: "Maybe you can work these off in exercise, instead." [53] (Other unhealthy habits the booklet preaches against are skipping breakfast, getting insufficient sleep, drinking more than moderately, and smoking.)

Blue Cross/Blue Shield, of course, is not interested in the public's health out of sheer altruism. It has apparently become impressed with the fact that when the smoker goes to smokEnders, the overweight person to Weight Watchers, and the unfit person to the Y, the health insurer, which has no obligation to pay for such health-promoting activities, benefits in the long run, because such customers have fewer illnesses. More generally, the steadily increasing proportion of the gross national product eaten up by expenditures on medical care (rising from 4.6 percent of GNP in fiscal 1950 to 8.6 percent in fiscal 1976[54]) has caused something approaching panic in both governmental and industrial circles and has made enormously attractive the idea of individuals and lay groups serving functions of disease prevention and simple medical care. A directory of health education activities issued by the Department of Health, Education, and Welfare waxes ecstatically that "the 'now' patient is increasingly an individual who can—just as in the days of the medical compendium on the kitchen shelf—do a great deal of health care for himself. . . . He can be motivated to be, quite literally, an assistant in his own treatment—a paramedical member of his own health care delivery team." [55] The publication does not explain that the "now" patient is expected to relieve the growing strain that medical expenditures represent on both public and private resources; others have noted, however, that "it is not at all surprising that we are presented an ideology which places responsibility on the individual at a time of economic strategy which urges cost containment and cutbacks on public resources." [56]

Some have noticed further that the messages coming from the powers that be are not always consistent. *Our Bodies,*

Ourselves points out: "Doctors want patients to do breast self-examination to detect cancer, but don't want them to get involved in decisions about breast cancer treatment. . . . Public-health officials don't want people to smoke or eat junk foods, but they don't publicly oppose advertising and research designed to 'prove' that such products are all right." [57] More insidiously, neither the medical nor the public-health establishment is willing to acknowledge that it is not out of individual perversity that people drive to work, sit (or stand in one place) all day, and eat too much salt, too much sugar, and an enormous assortment of chemicals for breakfast, lunch, and dinner; it is, in fact, only by acts of individual perversity that some people manage to avoid doing these unhealthy things.

But perhaps the most ironic twist of the dilemma of self-help and self-care is that the manifestation that is most challenging to the biomedical model and the commodification of healing—the women's health movement—is by the same token the most limited. Gynecological self-help, that is to say, deals largely with situations (childbirth and birth control) that, despite their incorporation into the biomedical model, are not really sicknesses at all. There is, of course, a value in chipping away at the encroachment of the biomedical model into areas where people are not even sick, but that tactic fails to benefit those who are undeniably sick but who resent the denial of their humanity that the incorporation of their sickness into the biomedical model entails. The gynecological self-help groups also differ from groups of, say, colostomy patients or even mastectomy patients in that their members can either escape feeling stigmatized altogether or can feel that dealing with the sense in which womanhood is a stigma is a matter of fighting against oppression. Finally, so long as the larger society is in some sense sexist, the women's health movement will not be taken seriously unless and until it goes beyond dealing with conditions that are uniquely female, unless it develops an approach as applicable to the person with an inflamed appendix as to the person with an infected vagina.

But then the self-help/self-care approach in general fumbles in the face of a heart attack, a broken hip, or any other acute, severe illness or injury. Its uplifting rhetoric about release from passivity and dependency is just noise to a person whose pain and anxiety are threatening to overwhelm his capacity for rational thought.[58] Its conception of the doctor as having "an educational relationship with patients rather than the traditional therapeutic one" [59] overlooks the impossibility of a single doctor-patient model being functional for all sickness situations and adopts the fallacy of assuming that trusting a healer to take on a leadership role in a crisis is identical to submitting, childlike, to an overweaning authoritarian figure.[60]

Conversely, no conception of the doctor-patient dyad, however egalitarian, can by itself heal the rift between the human experience of sickness and the dehumanizing view of disease that is the biomedical model. The most active, conscientious patient, self-educated in all the counterindications against antibiotics and the need for a second opinion before surgery, becomes a conspirator against his own humanity when he swallows an ideology that converts the struggle of his physical self with the stresses of living into an objectified symptom that has an independent existence.

Thus, the problem of the medical reformers is their failure, for the most part, to perceive the ideological component of medical practice, much less to perceive their state of being trapped by it. Their ultimate problem is that the ideology of medicine is only one pattern in the larger social fabric, that the commodification of healing is only a logical extension of the commodification of everything else. Blaming medical reformism thus, in the end, becomes itself a case of blaming the victim, for medical reformism is both a product and a victim of established economic, social, and political forces. Self-help and self-care, for example, are products of the social order in performing functions that are neither profitable nor otherwise valuable to either medical institutions or economic institutions; at the same time, they are victimized by the social order when their best features are co-opted to relieve the escalating burden of medical costs.

The final vicious circle becomes this: what makes the structure of medical practice increasingly problematic is its growing congruence with what is problematic about the larger society, while the attempts by the victims to reform the problematic features of modern medicine are themselves spawned and then distorted by the problematic features of the larger society. And the established institutions of the larger society have demonstrated enormous adaptive abilities to deflect a challenge or a potential challenge into a self-serving distortion of its initial thrust—as in corporations encouraging their executives to meditate on the job, the better not to notice that their work and what it represents has created the need for such a stress-reducing maneuver in the first place. The ultimate delusion, then, is to believe that humane and humanistic medicine is possible in the context of a society in which simply being human is more and more a struggle and human community more and more an illusion.

Notes

Introduction

1. Don E. Detmer and Helen H. Conrad, "Reflections upon Directive Language in Health Care," *Social Science and Medicine* 9:553–58 at p. 554 (October 1975). A more whimsical reaction to this linguistic trend is that " 'health delivery' became the catchword. At times it almost seemed as if the welcome wagon was supposed to roll up to the door and deliver health, wrapped in a neat package." Aaron Wildavsky, "Doing Better and Feeling Worse: The Political Pathology of Health Policy," *Daedalus, Proceedings of the American Academy of Arts and Sciences* 106:105–24 at p. 112 (Winter 1977).
2. George Orwell, "Politics and the English Language," in Sonia Orwell and Ian Agnus (eds.), *The Collected Essays, Journalism and Letters of George Orwell*, Vol. IV, *In Front of Your Nose*, pp. 127–40 at p. 137.

1 / From Unhappy Patient to Angry Litigant

1. "The Most Important Countersuit Victory Yet," *Medical Economics* 53(19):198–212 (September 20, 1976).
2. On the universe of medical injuries: "Studies which quantify injury rates are not the norm despite an extensive literature in medicine and in law that describes what types of harm occur from diagnostic tests, surgical procedures, and the various and sundry therapies and treatment regimens. . . . The reasons for the information gap with respect to injuries include the fragmentation in the health care delivery system, the economic and psychological disincentives in our society for gathering data on

mistakes and the legitimate interest of practitioners in the causes of injuries and their elimination rather than the gathering of statistics. The result is that the size and character of the injury universe is left to conjecture." Buddy Steves, "Medical Malpractice in Perspective," *CPCU Annals* 28:209–23 at pp. 210–11 (December 1975).

3. James L. Peterson, "Consumers' Knowledge of and Attitudes Toward Medical Malpractice," in *Appendix, Report of the Secretary's Commission on Medical Malpractice* (Washington, D.C.: U.S. Department of Health, Education, and Welfare, 1973), pp. 658–757 at pp. 669–88.

4. "Malpractice Poll: People Back MDs," *Medical World News* 16(17):27–29 at p. 27 (August 11, 1975).

5. Steves, *op. cit.,* p. 210.

6. George F. Newman, "Psychiatrists' Art Has Lessons for All M.D.s," *Michigan Medicine* 74:273–74 at p. 274 (May 1975).

7. Richard H. Blum, *The Management of the Doctor-Patient Relationship* (New York: McGraw-Hill Book Co., 1960), p. 253. (Italics in the original.)

8. Eli P. Bernzweig (then Executive Director, [HEW] Secretary's Commission on Medical Malpractice), "The Revenge Factor in Litigation," in Donald McDonald (ed.), *Medical Malpractice: A Center Occasional Paper* (Santa Barbara, California: Center for the Study of Democratic Institutions, 1971), p. 4.

9. "How to Avoid Malpractice Suits," *Medical World News* 16(20):61–72 at pp. 65, 62 (September 22, 1975), quoting John J. Bower.

10. Howard Eisenberg, "New Light on the Costliest Malpractice Mistakes," *Medical Economics* 50(17):146–63 at p. 163 (August 20, 1973), quoting Richard D. Hall, President, Empire Casualty Company.

11. Kenneth R. Mitchell, "Matrix for Malpractice: Tacit Contract Between Physicians and Patients," *Malpractice Digest,* published by St. Paul Fire and Marine Insurance Company (Summer 1975), pp. 1–3 at p. 3.

12. Jack E. Horsley and John Carlova, "Beware These Collection Pitfalls," *Medical Economics* 53(23):130–35 at p. 130 (November 1, 1976).

13. "How to Avoid Malpractice Suits," *op. cit.,* p. 64, quoting James J. McCabe.

14. Robert P. Fry, "How to Thwart Those Borderline Malpractice

Claims," *Medical Economics* 52(1)204–18 at p. 204 (January 6, 1975).

15. Blum, *op. cit.*, p. 136.

16. "An average [of] 15 per cent of all patients fail to pay their doctor's bills. The main reason why patients fail to pay their doctor bills is that these patients are angry with their doctor." *Ibid.*, p. xiii.

17. A 1976 survey of patient attitudes sponsored by *Medical Economics* found that 52 percent had stopped going to a doctor at one time or another because they disliked something about him, his methods, or his assistants. That proportion of patients switching doctors was an increase from 44 percent in the 1969 survey and 38 percent in 1963. Joel H. Goldberg, "Why More Patients Are Switching," *Medical Economics* 53(25):48–58 at p. 48 (November 29, 1976). A more scholarly study reported in 1976 found that 62 percent of 632 households in Salt Lake City (in four census tracts, two each comprising upper-middle and low socioeconomic neighborhoods) were doctor-shoppers, defined as people who at some time had changed doctors of their own volition (64 percent of the high-socioeconomic-status sample, 58 percent of the low). Fifty-three percent of the high- and 51 percent of the low-socioeconomic-status sample who changed doctors did so because they could not get an appointment within a week; 49 percent of the high- and 44 percent of the low-socioeconomic-status doctor-shoppers changed because the first doctor was not helping them. Donna M. Olsen et al., "Medical Care As a Commodity: An Exploration of the Shopping Behavior of Patients," *Journal of Community Health* 2:85–91 (Winter 1976).

18. "Despite the attacks of the American Medical Association designed to eliminate and regulate such competitors, nonscientific systems of healing have persisted and continue to be recognized and used, in part, because the physician has frequently failed to use effectively his role in treating the whole man. The chiropractor, the spiritual healer, the Christian Science practitioner, and many other nonscientific healers are frequently more attuned than physicians to the psychological needs of their client." David Mechanic, *Medical Sociology: A Selective View* (New York: The Free Press, 1968), p. 176.

19. A study in which 800 doctor-patient exchanges at the emergency clinic of Children's Hospital in Los Angeles (the mother

being defined as the patient) were recorded and interviews with the patients were conducted thereafter to determine the degree of compliance with physician instructions found: "Only 54 of the 800 patients seriously questioned the physician's technical competence (in their postvisit interviews with us), but failure to show a friendly interest or to fulfill their other expectations was a significant deterrent to compliance with his instructions. Of the patients who felt that the physician had not met any of their expectations, 56 percent were grossly noncompliant." Barbara M. Korsch and Vida Francis Negrete, "Doctor-Patient Communication," *Scientific American* 227(2):66–74 at p. 72 (August 1972).

20. Rosemary Stevens, *American Medicine and the Public Interest* (New Haven: Yale University Press, 1971), p. 374. (Italics in the original.)

21. Elihu M. Gerson, "The Social Character of Illness: Deviance or Politics?", *Social Science and Medicine* 10:219–24 at p. 220 (May 1976).

22. The classic statement of the sick role, including the social requirement that a sick person seek help from a technically trained person, is by Talcott Parsons; see Chapter X of *The Social System* (Glencoe, Ill.: The Free Press, 1951), Chapter 10 of *Social Structure and Personality* (New York: The Free Press, 1970), and "Illness and the Role of the Physician: A Sociological Perspective," in Clyde Kluckhohn and Henry A. Murray (eds.), *Personality in Nature, Society and Culture* (rev. ed.) (New York: Alfred A. Knopf, 1956).

23. Blum, *op. cit.,* p. 171.

24. Parsons, *The Social System, op. cit.,* p. 442.

25. Carol Taylor, *In Horizontal Orbit: Hospitals and the Cult of Efficiency* (New York: Holt, Rinehart and Winston, 1970), p. 126.

26. Marc H. Hollender, *The Psychology of Medical Practice* (Philadelphia: W. B. Saunders Co., 1958), p. 18.

27. Arthur K. Shapiro, "Factors Contributing to the Placebo Effect: Their Implications for Psychotherapy," *American Journal of Psychotherapy* 18(supplement 1):73–88 at p. 77 (March 1964).

28. Blum, *op. cit.,* p. 111.

2 / The Setting of Modern Medical Practice

1. U.S. Bureau of the Census, *Statistical Abstract of the United States: 1976* (Washington, D.C.: U.S. Government Printing Office, 1976), p. 84, Table 130. Admissions is a more relevant statistic for our purpose than patient days, given the trend toward declining patient days per admission; thus, patient days per 1,000 population in non-federal short-term hospitals increased only 33 percent from 1950 to 1973, from 900 to 1,194. Cambridge Research Institute, *Trends Affecting the U.S. Health Care System* (Washington, D.C.: U.S. Government Printing Office, 1976), p. 317. Absolute numbers of admissions is of course a misleading statistic because it fails to incorporate the effect of population growth.

2. *Statistical Abstract, op. cit.,* p. 81, Table 125.

3. Calculated from data at *ibid.*

4. Cambridge Research Institute, *op. cit.,* p. 63, Supplementary Exhibit S-1-6.

5. John H. Knowles, "The Hospital," *Scientific American* 229(3): 128–37 at p. 130 (September 1973).

6. A study of 24,158 malpractice claims closed between July 1, 1975, and June 30, 1976, found that 79 percent of claims closed with payment (the figure for total claims is not given) reflected incidents occurring in a hospital (including the emergency room), whether a physician, the hospital, or both were named as defendants. National Association of Insurance Commissioners, *Malpractice Claims No. 4* (Milwaukee: The Association, 1977), p. 40, Table 10a. Another closed-claims study, covering 9,164 claims closed in 1974, found that 81.4 percent of the claims (whether or not payment was made) reflected incidents that occurred somewhere in a hospital. Insurance Services Office, *Report to the All-Industry Committee, Special Malpractice Review: 1974 Closed Claim Survey, Preliminary Analysis of Survey Results* (New York: American Insurance Association, 1975), p. 33.

7. Cambridge Research Institute, *op. cit.,* pp. 91–92.

8. Marjorie Smith Mueller, "Private Health Insurance in 1973: A Review of Coverage, Enrollment, and Financial Experience," *Social Security Bulletin* 38(2):21–40 at p. 26, Table 6 (February 1975).

9. Talcott Parsons and Renée C. Fox, "Illness, Therapy and the Modern Urban American Family," *Journal of Social Issues* 8:31–44 (1952), reprinted in Norman W. Bell and Ezra F. Vogel (eds.), *A Modern Introduction to the Family* (New York: The Free Press, 1968), pp. 377–90.

10. Knowles, *op. cit.,* p. 128.

11. Leo H. Simmons and Harold G. Wolff, *Social Science in Medicine* (New York: Russell Sage Foundation, 1954), p. 171; Leon Lewis and Rose L. Coser, "The Dangers of Hospitalization," in Richard H. Blum, *Hospitals and Patient Dissatisfaction: A Study of Factors Associated with Malpractice Rates in Hospitals* (California Medical Association, 1958), pp. 303–32 at p. 306.

12. Raymond S. Duff and August B. Hollingshead, *Sickness and Society* (New York: Harper & Row, 1968), p. 154 ("Admission to the semiprivate accommodations [at Yale-New Haven Hospital], particularly on the medical service, was arranged frequently by the patient's physician so that he might obtain a consultation with another physician. Although a consultation with a selected specialist might have solved the problem, the consultation was not sought outside the hospital by the patient or his physician. The anxieties of patients, combined with the uncertainties of physicians, produced a crisis which to both the patient and the physician justified admission."); see also pp. 134–36, 177.

13. *Ibid.,* pp. 62, 372–73.

14. Rosemary Stevens, *American Medicine and the Public Interest* (New Haven: Yale University Press, 1971), p. 380.

15. "Surgery: Consumers Beware," *Health Perspectives* 3(5):1–8 at p. 4 (September–October 1976); Walter E. O'Donnell, "Who's Guilty of Overhospitalization? Me—and Probably You," *Medical Economics* 52(21):80–85 at p. 84 (October 13, 1975).

16. Simmons and Wolff, *op. cit.;* Lewis and Coser, *op. cit.* One sociological study of hospitals (sponsored by the American Hospital Association) treats the question of control by hospitalization by noting the disadvantages of treating patients on an outpatient basis in the hospital's clinics: "This [disadvantage] is the loss of leverage which follows from the patient's independence of the hospital system. The client does not stay, does not give up the clothing which lends him individuality, in short fails to become a fully adjusted patient. He brushes against the or-

ganization but never becomes a real part of it, while the in-patient enters the system more or less fully as soon as he occupies a bed." Temple Burling, Edith M. Lentz, and Robert N. Wilson, *The Give and Take in Hospitals: A Study of Human Organization in Hospitals* (New York: G. P. Putnam's Sons, 1956), p. 273.

17. The discussion of what hospitalization does to a person draws in part on the following sources: Richard H. Blum, *The Management of the Doctor-Patient Relationship* (New York: McGraw-Hill Book Co., 1960), pp. 219, 225; Esther Lucille Brown, "Meeting Patients' Psychosocial Needs in the General Hospital," in James K. Skipper, Jr., and Robert C. Leonard, *Social Interaction and Patient Care* (Philadelphia: J. B. Lippincott Co., 1965), pp. 6–15 at p. 9; Simmons and Wolff, *op. cit.,* p. 180; Rose Laub Coser, *Life in the Ward* (East Lansing, Mich.: Michigan State University Press, 1962), p. 41; Lewis and Coser, *op. cit.,* p. 304; Robert Sommer and Robert Dewar, "The Physical Environment of the Ward," in Eliot Freidson (ed.), *The Hospital in Modern Society* (Glencoe, Ill.: The Free Press, 1963), pp. 319–42 at p. 323; Daisy L. Tagliacozzo and Hans O. Mauksch, "The Patient's View of the Patient's Role," in E. Gartly Jaco, *Patients, Physicians and Illness* (2d ed.) (New York: The Free Press, 1972), pp. 172–85 at pp. 172–73; Albert F. Wessen, "Hospital Ideology and Communication Between Ward Personnel," in *ibid.,* pp. 325–42 at p. 326.

18. Duff and Hollingshead, *op. cit.,* p. 277 and p. 234, Table 30.

19. James K. Skipper, Jr., "Communication and the Hospitalized Patient," in Skipper and Leonard, *op. cit.,* pp. 61–82 at pp. 71–72.

20. Sommer and Dewar, *op. cit.,* p. 324.

21. Blum, *op. cit.,* p. 223.

22. Derward Lepley, Jr. (M.D.), " 'Treat Me Like a Patient, I Said,' " *American Medical News,* April 26, 1976, p. Impact/9.

23. Carol Taylor, *In Horizontal Orbit: Hospitals and the Cult of Efficiency* (New York: Holt, Rinehart and Winston, 1970), p. 65.

24. Duff and Hollingshead, *op. cit.,* p. 375.

25. William A. Glaser, "American and Foreign Hospitals: Some Sociological Comparisons," in Freidson, *op. cit.,* pp. 37–72 at p. 49.

26. Isabel E. P. Menzies, "A Case-Study in the Functioning of Social Systems as a Defence against Anxiety: A Report on a

Study of the Nursing Service of a General Hospital," *Human Relations* 13:95–121 at p. 101 (May 1960).

27. Duff and Hollingshead, *op. cit.*, pp. 226, 227; see also p. 374.
28. Burling, Lentz, and Wilson, *op. cit.*, p. 153. The fragmentation of hospital workers into large numbers of categories other than doctors and nurses and the effect of that fragmentation on patients are considered in Chapter 4.
29. Wessen, *op. cit.*, p. 28; see also Duff and Hollingshead, *op. cit.*, pp. 374, 376.
30. "Patient Safety Approach to Professional Liability: The Fellowship Breakfast from the 1977 ACS Spring Meeting," *Bulletin of the American College of Surgeons* 62(7):7–14 at p. 13, quoting Dr. William F. Donaldson, Co-chairman of the Prevention Subcommittee of the American Bar Association Commission on Medical Professional Liability.
31. Mary D. Hemelt and Mary Ellen Mackert, "Factual Medical Records Protect Hospitals, Practitioners, Patients," *Hospitals* 51(13):50–52 at p. 51 (July 1, 1977).
32. James K. Skipper, Jr., Daisy L. Tagliacozzo, and Hans O. Mauksch, "Some Possible Consequences of Limited Communication Between Patients and Hospital Functionaries," *Journal of Health and Human Behavior* 5:34–39 at pp. 34–35 (Spring 1964). The old open wards apparently served more broadly therapeutic functions as well. A doctor at the U.S. Public Health Service Hospital in Baltimore, where open wards are combined with semiprivate and private rooms without regard to income, has observed that "a substantial number, particularly younger patients, are obviously more comfortable on the wards and ask to be returned to the ward if they are placed in a private room immediately after surgery. We also notice dramatic deterioration in some withdrawn and disoriented patients if they are taken off the ward. The ward, even though it lacks that privacy which is something of an American fetish, seems to offer something very important to a number of patients." Stephen F. Jencks, "Problems in Participatory Health Care," in *Self-Help and Health: A Report* (New York: New Human Services Institute, 1976), pp. 85–98 at p. 92.
33. Skipper, "Communication and the Hospitalized Patient," *op. cit.*, p. 74.
34. *Ibid.*, p. 72, quoting a patient.
35. National Association of Insurance Commissioners, *op. cit.*, Table 13a, p. 65.

36. Reported in Michael R. Cohen, "Medication Error Reports," *Hospital Pharmacy* 10:202–3 at p. 202 (May 1975).

37. Reported in Michael R. Cohen, "Medication Error Reports," *Hospital Pharmacy* 11:242–43 at p. 242 (June 1976).

38. Reported in Michael R. Cohen, "Medication Error Reports," *Hospital Pharmacy* 11:146–48 at p. 146 (April 1976).

39. One study of medication errors found that most occurred during a period of the day when there was the greatest potential for distraction. George H. Lowrey, "The Problem of Hospital Accidents to Children," *Pediatrics* 32:1064–68 at p. 1066 (December 1963).

40. Reported in Michael R. Cohen, "Medication Error Reports," *Hospital Pharmacy* 10:166 (April 1975).

41. Neil M. Davis, "Editorial: Our Medication Error Report Feature," *Hospital Pharmacy* 10:180 (May 1975).

42. Health Law Center, *Problems in Hospital Law* (2d ed.) (Rockville, Md.: Aspen Systems Corp., 1974), pp. 44–45.

43. John V. Bennett et al., "Current National Patterns—United States," in *Proceedings of the International Conference on Nosocomial Infections,* Center for Disease Control, Atlanta, August 5–6, 1970 (Chicago: American Hospital Association, 1971), pp. 42–49 at pp. 42, 46.

44. American Hospital Association, *Infection Control in the Hospital* (rev. ed.) (Chicago: The Association, 1970), at p. 1 states: "Over 13 per cent of the patients in one large community hospital recently surveyed had developed infections while in the hospital."

45. Crawford Morris, "Nosocomial Infections and the Law," in *Proceedings, op. cit.,* pp. 322–30 at p. 325.

46. William H. L. Dornette, "Legal Aspects of Hospital-Acquired Infections," *Journal of Legal Medicine* 1:27–31 at p. 27 (May/June 1973).

47. Rudolf G. Wanner, in foreword to Elaine C. Dubay and Reba D. Grubb, *Infection Prevention and Control* (St. Louis: C. V. Mosby Co., 1973), p. vii.

48. Joint Commission on Accreditation of Hospitals, *Accreditation Manual for Hospitals* (Chicago: The Commission, 1976), p. 50 (Infection Control, Standard II).

49. "What Hospitals Are Doing to Cut Down Accidents," *U.S. News & World Report* (March 29, 1976), pp. 36–38 at p. 36.

50. Dubay and Grubb, *op. cit.,* p. ix.

51. There may be a disparity between the target or targets of the

patient's anger and the named defendants in a malpractice suit for reasons having to do with the state of the law and/or the tactics preferred by the lawyer.

52. E.g., Duff and Hollingshead, *op. cit.*, pp. 269, 272; Charles S. Houston and Wayne E. Pasanen, "Patients' Perceptions of Hospital Care," *Hospitals* 46(8):70–74 at p. 73 (April 16, 1972); Ernest Dichter, "A Psychological Study of the Hospital-Patient Relationship: What the Patient Really Wants from the Hospital," *Modern Hospital* 83(2):51–54 at pp. 52, 53–54 (September 1954).

53. Skipper, "Communication and the Hospitalized Patient," *op. cit.*, pp. 62–64; Ernest Dichter, "A Psychological Study of the Hospital-Patient Relationship: How to Make Your Hospital 'Secure,'" *Modern Hospital* 83(6):69–73 at p. 69 (December 1954); Duff and Hollingshead, *op. cit.*, pp. 207–8; Ernest Dichter, "A Psychological Study of the Hospital-Patient Relationship: The Patient's Greatest Need Is Security," *Modern Hospital* 83(4):56–58, 134 at p. 57 (October 1954).

54. Quoted in Daisy L. Tagliacozzo, "The Nurse from the Patient's Point of View," in Skipper and Leonard, *op. cit.*, pp. 219–27 at p. 223.

55. Cohen, May 1975, *op. cit.*, p. 202; as the nurse was leaving the room, the patient inquired, "Don't I get any ear drops?"

56. Quoted in Simmons and Wolff, *op. cit.*, p. 181. (Italics in the original.)

57. Quoted in Skipper, Tagliacozzo, and Mauksch, *op. cit.*, p. 38.

58. Duff and Hollingshead, *op. cit.*, pp. 269–70; see also p. 376 ("Though reactions may have been withheld by the patients or not perceived by professionals, patient resentments were common. They were centered primarily upon disappointment in the physician, especially in his failure to communicate").

59. Ailon Shiloh, "Equalitarian and Hierarchal Patients: An Investigation among Hadassah Hospital Patients," in Eliot Freidson and Judith Lorber, *Medical Men and Their Work* (Chicago: Aldine-Atherton, Inc., 1972), pp. 249–66 at p. 256. A similar twofold classification of hospital patients is made by Taylor, *op. cit.*, pp. 69–70.

60. Blum, *Hospitals and Patient Dissatisfaction, op. cit.*, p. 3, discussing the findings of two earlier (unpublished) studies.

3 / The Tools of Modern Medical Practice

1. Bernard Jacobs, M.D., quoted in "A Roundtable on Medical Malpractice" (transcription of a panel discussion), *New York Affairs* 2(3):90–127 at p. 95 (Spring 1975).
2. Office of Technology Assessment, U.S. Congress, *Development of Medical Technology: Opportunities for Assessment* (Washington, D.C.: U.S. Government Printing Office, 1976), pp. 10–11. (The machine alluded to is the Sequential Multiple-Analyzer with Computer, or SMAC, introduced in 1973.)
3. Jerry E. Bishop, "Medical Advances and the Growth of Insurance Dim Hopes of Curbing Rising Health-Care Costs," *The Wall Street Journal*, February 17, 1977, p. 38.
4. Alan Sheldon, "The Efficient Humanist," in William J. Abernathy, Alan Sheldon, and Coimbatore K. Prahalad, *The Management of Health Care* (Cambridge, Mass.: Ballinger Publishing Co., 1974), pp. 281–90 at p. 282.
5. Clifton K. Meador, "The Art and Science of Nondisease," *New England Journal of Medicine* 272:92–95 at p. 94 (January 14, 1965), reprinted in Eliot Freidson and Judith Lorber (eds.), *Medical Men and Their Work* (Chicago: Aldine-Atherton, Inc., 1972).
6. Seymour Handler, "Bring Back the Mustard Plaster," *Minnesota Medicine* 54:973–79 at p. 974 (December 1971).
7. Alex M. Burgess and Alex M. Burgess, Jr., "Caring for the Patient—A Thrice-Told Tale," *New England Journal of Medicine* 274:1241–44 at p. 1242 (June 2, 1966).
8. Victor Fuchs, "The Growing Demand for Medical Care," *New England Journal of Medicine* 279:190–95 at p. 193 (July 25, 1968). (Italics in the original.)
9. *Ibid.*, p. 192.
10. Robert Ray McGee, "Let's Fall Out of Love with Our New Technology," *Medical Economics* 53(3):153–58 at p. 155 (February 9, 1976).
11. Talcott Parsons, *The Social System* (Glencoe, Ill.: The Free Press, 1951), p. 466.
12. John P. Bunker, "Surgical Manpower: A Comparison of Operations and Surgeons in the United States and in England and Wales," *New England Journal of Medicine* 282:135–44 at p. 140 (January 15, 1970).

202 *Notes to Pages 39–41*

13. Paul B. Beeson, "The Ways of Academic Clinical Medicine in America since World War II," *Man and Medicine* 1:65–79 at p. 66 (Autumn 1975).
14. Rosemary Stevens, *American Medicine and the Public Interest* (New Haven: Yale University Press, 1971), p. 360.
15. Marjorie Smith Mueller and Robert M. Gibson, "National Health Expenditures, Fiscal Year 1975," *Social Security Bulletin* 39(2):3–21 at p. 12, Table 4, and p. 20 (February 1976).
16. Cambridge Research Institute, *Trends Affecting the U.S. Health Care System* (Washington, D.C.: U.S. Government Printing Office, 1976), p. 208, Exhibit IV–8.
17. The conventional wisdom is that the increase in morbidity and mortality from chronic disease is a by-product of scientific advance in treating acute disease, people now surviving the latter eventually to succumb to the former. A critique of this theory pointedly notes that "if this were so, one would expect the highest death rates from chronic disease in that part of the population with the longest life expectancy and the best medical care. . . . Precisely the opposite is true. Black death rates for chronic diseases are in almost all cases higher than the white death rates despite the fact that blacks have poorer medical care and higher death rates at all ages from acute as well as chronic causes." Joseph Eyer and Peter Sterling, "Stress-Related Mortality and Social Organization," *The Review of Radical Political Economics* 9(1):1–44 at p. 6 (Spring 1977).
18. Cambridge Research Institute, *op. cit.,* p. 322, Exhibit IV–12; American Hospital Association, *Hospital Statistics, 1976 Edition*, Table 12A, pp. 188–95.
19. Parsons, *op. cit.,* pp. 467–68; Kenneth E. Warner, "A 'Desperation-Reaction Model' of Medical Diffusion," *Health Services Research* 10:369–83 (Winter 1975).
20. W. J. Abernathy and C. K. Prahalad, "Technology and Productivity in Health Organizations," in Abernathy et al., *op. cit.,* pp. 189–203 at p. 195. (At the time of writing, Abernathy was an associate professor of business administration at the Harvard Business School and Prahalad was a research associate and doctoral candidate there.)
21. Richard J. Hess and Herbert B. McDonald, "Diseases of Diagnostic Procedures," in Robert H. Moser (ed.), *Diseases of Medical Progress: A Study of Iatrogenic Disease* (3d ed.) (Springfield: Charles C. Thomas, 1969), pp. 709–808 at p. 710.
22. Office of Technology Assessment, *op. cit.,* pp. 16–17.

23. Howard H. Hiatt, "Too Much Medical Technology?", *The Wall Street Journal,* June 24, 1976, p. 14.
24. Howard H. Hiatt, "Protecting the Medical Commons: Who Is Responsible?", *New England Journal of Medicine* 293:235–41 at p. 237 (July 31, 1975); Walsh McDermott, "Evaluating the Physician and His Technology," *Daedalus, Proceedings of the American Academy of Arts and Sciences* 106:135–58 at p. 145 (Winter 1977).
25. James L. Goddard, "The Medical Business," *Scientific American* 229(3):161–66 at p. 161 (September 1973).
26. Jane Brody, "Experts Give Advice on Blood Pressure," *The New York Times,* February 13, 1977, p. 27.
27. There is, in fact, a 900-odd page, admittedly incomplete, medical treatise on the risk aspect of the problem—Robert H. Moser (ed.), *Diseases of Medical Progress: A Study of Iatrogenic Disease* (3d ed.) (Springfield: Charles C. Thomas, 1969).
28. Elihu M. Schimmel, "Hazards of Hospitalization," *Annals of Internal Medicine* 60:100–16 at p. 108 (January 1964).
29. Hess and McDonald, *op. cit.,* p. 709.
30. *Ibid.*
31. *Ibid.,* p. 781.
32. Schimmel, *op. cit.,* pp. 101–2, 105. (The study was conducted at the Yale University Medical Service of Grace-New Haven Community Hospital.)
33. Sherman M. Mellinkoff, "Chemical Intervention," *Scientific American* 229(3):103–12 at p. 103 (September 1973).
34. Milton Silverman and Philip R. Lee, *Pills, Profits, and Politics* (Berkeley and Los Angeles: University of California Press, 1974), p. 5.
35. *Ibid.*
36. *Ibid.,* pp. 16, 17.
37. Ingrid Waldron, "Prescribing of Valium, Librium, and Other Drugs—An Example of the Influence of Economic and Social Factors on the Practice of Medicine," *International Journal of Health Services* 7:37–62 at p. 53 (1977).
38. Henry E. Simmons and Paul D. Stolley, "This Is Medical Progress? Trends and Consequences of Antibiotic Use in the United States," *Journal of the American Medical Association* 227:1023–28 at p. 1024 (March 4, 1974).
39. Silverman and Lee, *op. cit.,* p. 269.
40. Simmons and Stolley, *op. cit.,* p. 1024.
41. This paragraph draws on D. P. Barr, "Hazards of Modern Diag-

nosis and Therapy: The Price We Pay," *Journal of the American Medical Association* 159:52–56 (December 10, 1955); Stanley Newman and James F. Wallace, "Hypersensitivity and Connective Tissue Disorders," in Moser, *op. cit.*, pp. 418–35 at pp. 418–20; William C. Fisher, "Dermatologic Diseases," in *ibid.*, pp. 191–234 at p. 191; David W. Louisell and Harold Williams, *Medical Malpractice* (New York: Matthew Bender, 1973, with 1976 supplement), pp. 125–26, 573; Jane Porter and Hershel Jick, "Drug-Related Deaths among Medical Inpatients," *Journal of the American Medical Association* 237: 879–81 at p. 881 (February 28, 1977).

42. Silverman and Lee, *op. cit.*, p. 259.
43. *Ibid.*, p. 262.
44. *Ibid.*, p. 278.
45. *Ibid.*, p. 270; Robert C. Zurek, "Antibiotic-induced Diseases," in Moser, *op. cit.*, pp. 3–82 at p. 11.
46. Zurek, *op. cit.*, p. 15.
47. Silverman and Lee, *op. cit.*, p. 270.
48. William Hall, "Congenital Diseases," in Moser, *op. cit.*, pp. 163–90.
49. Porter and Jick, *op. cit.*, p. 879, Table 1.
50. Schimmel, *op. cit.*, pp. 102–3, 106.
51. J. T. McLamb and R. R. Huntley, "The Hazards of Hospitalization," *Southern Medical Journal* 60:469–72 at pp. 470, 471 (May 1967).
52. See references cited in George J. Caranasos, Ronald S. Stewart, and Leighton E. Cluff, "Drug-Induced Illness Leading to Hospitalization," *Journal of the American Medical Association* 228:713–17 at p. 713 (May 6, 1974).
53. *Ibid.*
54. See references cited *ibid.*, p. 716.
55. Simmons and Stolley, *op. cit.*, pp. 1024, 1026–27.
56. Jerome D. Frank, *Persuasion and Healing* (rev. ed.) (New York: Schocken Books, 1974), p. 138.
57. Handler, *op. cit.*, p. 974.
58. Marc H. Hollender, *The Psychology of Medical Practice* (Philadelphia: W. B. Saunders Co., 1958), p. 236.
59. Waldron, *op. cit.*, p. 57.
60. Franz J. Ingelfinger, "Drugs and the Anxious Patient," in Franz J. Ingelfinger, Richard V. Ebert, Maxwell Finland, and Arnold S. Relman, *Controversy in Internal Medicine II* (Philadelphia: W. B. Saunders Co., 1974), pp. 33–34 at p. 33.

61. Charlotte Muller, "The Overmedicated Society: Forces in the Marketplace for Medical Care," *Science* 176:488–92 at p. 490 (May 5, 1972). (Muller describes prescribing as a "termination strategy" by which the doctor limits the length of his appointments and thus avoids having either to extend his working day or to see fewer patients, which would reduce his income.)

62. James E. Eckenhoff, "Some Preoperative Warnings of Potential Operating-Room Deaths," *New England Journal of Medicine* 255:1075–79 at p. 1079 (December 6, 1956).

63. Charles G. Child III, "Surgical Intervention," *Scientific American* 229(3):91–98 at p. 91 (September 1973).

64. The 1949 figure is taken from "Special Information, 1949," *Hospitals* 24(6, Part 2):17 (June 1950); the 1975 figure, from National Center for Health Statistics, *Utilization of Short-Stay Hospitals: Annual Summary for the United States, 1975* (U.S. Department of Health, Education, and Welfare, Publication No. [HRA] 77–1782, April 1977), p. 15. Population figures are taken from the *Statistical Abstract of the United States*.

65. Cambridge Research Institute, *op. cit.,* p. 360, Exhibit IV–23 (surgical specialties comprised 28.7 percent of non-federal physicians in 1973).

66. National Center for Health Statistics, *op. cit.,* p. 15 (one or more surgical operations were performed on 41.7 percent of the inpatients discharged from non-federal short-stay hospitals during 1975).

67. A study of 24,158 malpractice claims closed between July 1, 1975, and June 30, 1976, found that 59.5 percent of claims closed with payment (the figure for total claims is not given) reflected incidents involving surgical procedures (including anesthesia). National Association of Insurance Commissioners, *Malpractice Claims No. 4* (Milwaukee: The Association, September 1977), Table 13a, p. 65 and Appendix B. Another closed-claims study, covering 9,164 claims closed in 1974, found that 63.7 percent of the claims (whether or not payment was made) were asserted against doctors with surgical insurance classifications. Insurance Services Office, *Report to the All-Industry Committee, Special Malpractice Review: 1974 Closed Claim Survey, Preliminary Analysis of Survey Results* (New York: American Insurance Association, 1975), p. 18.

68. Subcommittee on Oversight and Investigations, Committee on Interstate and Foreign Commerce, U.S. House of Representatives, *Cost and Quality of Health Care: Unnecessary Surgery,*

94th Congress, 2d Session, January 1976, Subcommittee Print, p. 33 (citing unpublished data of the National Center for Health Statistics and an estimate of the Commission on Professional and Hospital Activities, both arriving at 1.4 percent).

69. Frederick F. Cartwright, *The Development of Modern Surgery* (New York: Thomas Y. Crowell Co., 1967), p. 278.

70. Gordon Taylor, C. Philip Carson, Jr., and Ramune Prestwich, "Unexpected Cardiac Arrest during Anesthesia and Surgery," *Journal of the American Medical Association* 236:2758–60 (December 13, 1976).

71. Robert P. Bolande, "Ritualistic Surgery—Circumcision and Tonsillectomy," *New England Journal of Medicine* 280:591–96 at p. 593 (March 13, 1969).

72. John Joakim Skillman, "Postoperative Deep Vein Thrombosis and Pulmonary Embolism: A Selective Review and Personal Viewpoint," *Surgery* 75:114–22 at p. 114 (January 1974).

73. P. J. Morris, B. A. Barnes, and J. F. Burke, "The Nature of the Irreducible Minimum Rate of Incisional Sepsis," *Archives of Surgery* 92:367–70 (March 1966).

74. Zurek, *op. cit.*, p. 13.

75. Leon S. Pocincki, Stuart J. Dogger, and Barbara P. Schwartz, "The Incidence of Iatrogenic Injuries," in *Appendix, Report of the Secretary's Commission on Medical Malpractice* (Washington, D.C.: U.S. Department of Health, Education, and Welfare, 1973), pp. 50–70 at p. 55.

76. Parsons, *op. cit.*, pp. 466–67; see also Handler, *op. cit.*, p. 977. ("The problem created by referring a medical condition to a surgeon is similar to seeking investment advice from a stockbroker. . . . The broker does his thing—persuade the investor to buy and sell. The surgeon does his thing—operate.")

77. McDermott, *op. cit.*, pp. 144–45.

78. See, e.g., *ibid.*, p. 151; Richard V. Ebert, "Comment: Are Coronary Bypass Grafts the Answer to Angina Pectoris?", in Ingelfinger et al., *op. cit.*, p. 142; Hiatt, "Protecting the Medical Commons," *op. cit.*, p. 237; Duncan Neuhauser and Egon Jonsson, "Managerial Response to New Health Care Technology: Coronary Artery Bypass Surgery," in Abernathy et al., *op. cit.*, pp. 205–13; Marcia Millman, *The Unkindest Cut: Life in the Backrooms of Medicine* (New York: William Morrow & Co., 1977), appendix; Marvin L. Murphy et al., "Treatment of Chronic Stable Angina," *New England Journal of Medicine* 297:621–27 (September 22, 1977).

79. Bernard Kutner, "Surgeons and Their Patients," in E. Gartley Jaco (ed.), *Patients, Physicians and Illness* (New York: The Free Press, 1958), pp. 384–96 at p. 389.
80. Raymond S. Duff and August B. Hollingshead, *Sickness and Society* (New York: Harper & Row, 1968), p. 273.
81. Richard H. Blum, *The Management of the Doctor-Patient Relationship* (New York: McGraw-Hill Book Co., 1960), p. 49.
82. Irving L. Janis, *Psychological Stress: Psychoanalytic and Behavioral Studies of Surgical Patients* (New York: John Wiley & Sons, 1958), p. 214.
83. Bernard C. Meyer, "Some Psychiatric Aspects of Surgical Practice," *Psychosomatic Medicine* 20:203–14 at p. 207 (May–June 1958); see also James E. Eckenhoff, *op. cit.*, p. 1076. ("The markedly apprehensive patient is a potential candidate for death in the operating room. At least four times during the past ten years we have had patients who died during or immediately after operation, having evinced marked preoperative apprehension. . . . By ordinary standards none should have died.")
84. Robert Elman, *Surgical Care: A Practical Physiologic Guide* (New York: Appleton-Century-Crofts, 1951), p. 42.
85. Hollender, *op. cit.*, pp. 117–18; see also Thomas S. Szasz and Marc H. Hollender, "A Contribution to the Philosophy of Medicine: The Basic Models of the Doctor-Patient Relationship," *Archives of Internal Medicine* 97:585–91 at pp. 587–88 (May 1956).
86. Jerome D. Orenland, "A Psychiatrist Sits in the Operating Room: A Study of Anxiety and Inter-Personal Relationships Affecting Surgical Patients," in Richard H. Blum, *Hospitals and Patient Dissatisfaction: A Study of Factors Associated with Malpractice Rates in Hospitals* (California Medical Association, 1958), p. 298.
87. Donald McDonald (ed.), *Medical Malpractice: A Center Occasional Paper* (Santa Barbara, California: Center for the Study of Democratic Institutions, 1971), p. 2, quoting Roger Egeberg.
88. McGee, *op. cit.*, p. 155.
89. Duff and Hollingshead, *op. cit.*, p. 167.
90. *Ibid.*, p. 319.
91. Meyer, *op. cit.*, p. 203.

4 / The Agents of Modern
Medical Practice

1. Figures for 1950 from National Institutes of Health, *Health Manpower Source Book: Section 21, Allied Health Manpower, 1958–80* (1970), p. 4; for 1974 from National Center for Health Statistics, *Health Resources Statistics: Health Manpower and Health Facilities, 1975* (1976), pp. 9–10, Table 1.

2. Figures for 1974 calculated from *ibid.*, p. 173, Table 96; figures for 1949 from Rosemary Stevens, *American Medicine and the Public Interest* (New Haven: Yale University Press, 1971), p. 181, Table 2. (The category of surgical specialists includes anesthesiologists.)

3. *Ibid.*, pp. 279, 299, 300, 380, Table 4.

4. National Center for Health Statistics, *op. cit.*, calculated from Table 96, p. 173.

5. Paul B. Beeson, "The Ways of Academic Clinical Medicine in America since World War II," *Man and Medicine* 1:65–79 at p. 66 (Autumn 1975).

6. George A. Silver, *A Spy in the House of Medicine* (Germantown, Maryland: Aspen Systems Corp., 1976), p. 218; Robert H. Ebert, "Medical Education in the United States," *Daedalus, Proceedings of the American Academy of Arts and Sciences* 106:171–84 at p. 179 (Winter 1977).

7. Beeson, *op. cit.*, p. 72.

8. Robert H. Ebert, "The Medical School," *Scientific American* 229(3):139–48 at p. 141 (September 1973); Richard H. Magraw, *Ferment in Medicine: A Study of the Essence of Medical Practice and of Its New Dilemmas* (Philadelphia: W. B. Saunders Co., 1966), p. 151.

9. Rick J. Carlson, *The End of Medicine* (New York: John Wiley & Sons, 1975), p. 41.

10. Cambridge Research Institute, *Trends Affecting the U.S. Health Care System* (Washington, D.C.: U.S. Government Printing Office, 1976), p. 362.

11. Temple Burling, Edith M. Lentz, and Robert N. Wilson, *The Give and Take in Hospitals: A Study of Human Organization in Hospitals* (New York: G. P. Putnam's Sons, 1956), p. 105.

12. Figures for 1959 from Cambridge Research Institute, *op. cit.*, p. 403; for 1974 from National Center for Health Statistics, *op. cit.*, p. 201, Table 111.

13. Fred E. Katz, "Nurses," in Amitai Etzioni (ed.), *The Semi-Professions and Their Organization* (New York: The Free Press, 1969), pp. 54–81 at p. 71.

14. National Center for Health Statistics, *op. cit.*, p. 192.

15. Cambridge Research Institute, *op. cit.*, p. 309, Exhibit IV–31 and p. 400, Exhibit IV–32.

16. Figures for 1950 from National Institutes of Health, *op. cit.*, Table 2, p. 4; for 1974 from National Center for Health Statistics, *op. cit.*, Table 1, pp. 9–12.

17. Figure for 1974 from *ibid.*, p. 55; for 1950 from National Center for Health Statistics, *Health Resources Statistics: Health Manpower and Facilities, 1968* (1969), p. 53. (The numbers for each year, representing full-time or part-time employees, in addition to physicians, engaged in providing services in clinical laboratories, are about 30,000 in 1950 and 172,500 in 1974.)

18. National Center for Health Statistics, *1975 Health Resources Statistics, op. cit.*, p. 269.

19. Figure for 1950 from *Statistical Abstract of the United States: 1975* (Washington, D.C.: U.S. Government Printing Office, 1975), p. 79, Table 122; for 1974 from American Hospital Association, *Hospital Statistics, 1975 Edition*, p. xii. (Figures represent full-time-equivalent employees in all hospitals, excluding interns and residents.)

20. Figure for 1950 from *Statistical Abstract of the United States: 1969* (Washington, D.C.: U.S. Government Printing Office, 1969), p. 69; for 1974 from *Statistical Abstract of the United States: 1976* (Washington, D.C.: U.S. Government Printing Office, 1976), p. 82. (Figures are for non-federal short-term general hospitals and special hospitals other than psychiatric and tuberculosis hospitals; interns and residents are included in 1950 but excluded in 1974, i.e., the 1950 figure is higher than it should be.)

21. Bernard M. Weinstein and Doris Lesser, "Health Manpower," *Hospitals* 48(7):67–72 at p. 68 (April 1, 1974), citing a 1973 unpublished report of a committee of the American Hospital Association.

22. Robert N. Wilson, "The Social Structure of a General Hospital," in James K. Skipper, Jr., and Robert C. Leonard, *Social Interaction and Patient Care* (Philadelphia: J. B. Lippincott Co., 1965), pp. 233–44 at p. 240.

23. Robert N. Wilson, *The Sociology of Health* (New York: Random House, 1970), p. 38.

24. Wilson, "Social Structure," *op. cit.,* p. 241.
25. David Mechanic, "Some Social Aspects of the Medical Malpractice Dilemma," *Duke Law Journal* 1975:1179–96 at p. 1185 (January 1976).
26. Burling *et al., op. cit.,* p. 133.
27. Bonnie Burrough and Vern Burrough, "A Brief History of Medical Practice," in Eliot Freidson and Judith Lorber (eds.), *Medical Men and Their Work* (Chicago: Aldine-Atherton, Inc., 1972), pp. 86–112 at p. 101.
28. Magraw, *op. cit.,* p. 50.
29. Michael Balint, *The Doctor, the Patient and the Illness* (2d ed.) (London: Pitman Medical Publishing Co., Ltd., 1964), p. 92.
30. Raymond S. Duff and August B. Hollingshead, *Sickness and Society* (New York: Harper & Row, 1968), pp. 372–73.
31. *Ibid.,* p. 60.
32. George J. Caranasos, Ronald S. Stewart, and Leighton E. Cluff, "Drug-Induced Illness Leading to Hospitalization," *Journal of the American Medical Association* 228:713–17 at p. 717 (May 6, 1794).
33. Mark G. Field, "The Health Care System of Industrial Society: The Disappearance of the General Practitioner and Some Implications," in Everett Mendelsohn, Judith P. Swazey, and Irene Taviss (eds.), *Human Aspects of Biomedical Innovation* (Cambridge: Harvard University Press, 1971), pp. 156–80 at p. 171. In *Julia's Story* by Fred J. Cook (New York: Holt, Rinehart and Winston, 1976), the author relates the death of his wife, of which the immediate cause was hemorrhaging triggered by Coumadin, an anticoagulant. It is clear that a major contributing factor was a lack of coordination between her heart surgeon and her cardiologist, and the failure of either to assume responsibility for her care during a critical postoperative period.
34. Elihu M. Gerson, "The Social Character of Illness: Deviance or Politics?", *Social Science and Medicine* 10:219–24 at p. 222 (May 1976).
35. Daisy L. Tagliacozzo and Hans O. Mauksch, "The Patient's View of the Patient's Role," in E. Gartly Jaco (ed.), *Patients, Physicians, and Illness* (2d ed.) (New York: The Free Press, 1972), pp. 172–85 at p. 184.
36. Carol Taylor, *In Horizontal Orbit: Hospitals and the Cult of Efficiency* (New York: Holt, Rinehart and Winston, 1970), pp. 55–56.
37. Field, *op. cit.,* p. 172.

38. Esther Lucille Brown, "Meeting Patients' Psychosocial Needs in the General Hospital," in Skipper and Leonard, *op. cit.,* pp. 6–15 at pp. 10–11.

39. Eugene B. Gallagher, "Lines of Reconstruction and Extension in the Parsonian Sociology of Illness," *Social Science and Medicine* 10:207–18 at p. 213 (May 1976).

40. Quoted in Ernest Dichter, "A Psychological Study of the Hospital-Patient Relationship—The Patient's Greatest Need Is Security," *Modern Hospital* 83(4):56–58, 134 at p. 57 (October 1954).

41. Robert N. Wilson, "The Physician's Changing Hospital Role," *Human Organization* 18:177–83 at p. 179 (Winter 1959–60).

42. Field, *op. cit.,* p. 173.

43. Richard H. Blum, *The Management of the Doctor-Patient Relationship* (New York: McGraw-Hill Book Co., 1960), p. 244.

5 / The Financing of Modern Medical Practice

1. Brian Abel-Smith, "Value for Money in Health Services," *Social Security Bulletin* 37(7):17–28 at p. 25 (July 1974): "The fundamental question is whether it is the task of the physician simply to perform medical acts or to deliver comprehensive health care."

2. Subcommittee on Health, Committee on Ways and Means, U.S. House of Representatives, *National Health Insurance Resource Book* (rev. ed.) (Washington, D.C.: U.S. Government Printing Office, 1976), Chart 3g, pp. 50–51, citing American Medical Association Center for Health Services Resources and Development as its source.

3. U.S. Bureau of the Census, *Statistical Abstract of the United States: 1976* (Washington, D.C.: U.S. Government Printing Office, 1976), p. 383, Table 617 gives the 1974 median annual earnings for males in all occupations as $11,835; the figure for females is $6,772. The percentage of physicians who are male (the exact figure given is 92.1 percent) is taken from Vicente Navarro, *Medicine under Capitalism* (New York: PRODIST, 1976), p. 173.

4. Subcommittee on Health, *op. cit.,* pp. 50–51.

5. Maurice Fox (M.D.), "Why People Are Mad at Doctors," *Newsweek* (January 10, 1977), p. 4.

6. Quoted in Herman M. Somers and Anne R. Somers, *Doctors, Patients, and Health Insurance: The Organization and Financing of Medical Care* (Washington, D.C.: The Brookings Institution, 1961), p. 467.

7. Buddy Steves, "Medical Malpractice in Perspective," *CPCU Annals* 28:209–23 at p. 211 (December 1975).

8. Eliot Freidson, *Doctoring Together: A Study of Professional Social Control* (New York: Elsevier Scientific Publishing Co., 1975), pp. 60–62.

9. See, e.g., Subcommittee on Oversight and Investigations, Committee on Interstate and Foreign Commerce, U.S. House of Representatives, *Cost and Quality of Health Care: Unnecessary Surgery,* 94th Congress, 2d Session, January 1976, Subcommittee Print, pp. 13–15.

10. Richard M. Magraw, *Ferment in Medicine: A Study of the Essence of Medical Practice and of Its New Dilemmas* (Philadelphia: W. B. Saunders Co., 1966), p. 5. (Italics in the original.)

11. Abel-Smith, *op. cit.,* p. 22.

12. *Ibid.;* see also William A. Glaser, *Paying the Doctor: Systems of Remuneration and Their Effects* (Baltimore: Johns Hopkins Press, 1970), p. 254, n. 1: "The British general practitioners interviewed by a visiting American doctor said that the elimination of collections and the reduction of paper work were among the greatest merits of the National Health Service. Paul F. Gemmill, *Britain's Search for Health* (Philadelphia: University of Pennsylvania Press, 1960), pp. 123–25."

13. George D. LeMaitre (M.D.), "Sure Let's Strike—But Against Health Insurers," *Medical Economics* 53(4):97–109 at p. 101 (February 23, 1976).

14. Magraw, *op. cit.,* p. 192.

15. Freidson, *op. cit.,* p. 249. (Italics in the original.)

16. Letter from Robert M. Jay to *The New York Times,* June 9, 1976, p. 38.

17. Louise Lander, *National Health Insurance: He Who Pays the Piper Lets the Piper Call the Tune* (New York: Health Policy Advisory Center, 1975), pp. 5–6, 23, 15–19.

18. Herbert E. Klarman, "The Financing of Health Care," *Daedalus, Proceedings of the American Academy of Arts and Sciences* 106:215–34 at pp. 228–29 (Winter 1977).

19. Cambridge Research Institute, *Trends Affecting the U.S. Health*

Care System (Washington, D.C.: U.S. Government Printing Office, 1976), pp. 167, 173.

20. John Carlova, "Fees and Income: Is Resentment on the Rise?", *Medical Economics* 53(25):62–76 at p. 70 (November 29, 1976).

21. Edwin N. Perrin, "Are You the Kind of Physician Who Gets Sued?", *Medical Economics* 36(2):79–86 at p. 81 (January 19, 1959), reporting an unpublished study, "The Psychology of Malpractice Suits," conducted for the California Medical Association by Richard H. Blum, Ph.D.

22. "You—Through Your Patients' Eyes," *Medical Economics* 53(25):5–10 at pp. 5–6 (November 29, 1976).

23. Carlova, *op. cit.,* p. 63.

6 / The Ideology of Modern Medical Practice

1. This paragraph draws in part on George L. Engel, "The Need for a New Medical Model: A Challenge for Biomedicine," *Science* 196:129–36 at p. 130 (April 8, 1977); René Dubos, *Mirage of Health: Utopias, Progress, and Biological Change* (Garden City: Anchor/Doubleday, 1959), p. 91; Horacio Fabrega, Jr., "The Need for an Ethnomedical Science," *Science* 189:969–75 at pp. 969–70 (September 19, 1975).

2. Engel, *op. cit.,* p. 131. This paragraph also draws on Howard Rasmussen, "Medical Education—Revolution or Reaction," *The Pharos of Alpha Omega Alpha* 38:53–59 at p. 55 (April 1975).

3. This section draws on Dubos, *op. cit.,* pp. 68–69; John Powles, "On the Limitations of Modern Medicine," *Science, Medicine and Man* 1:1–30 at p. 15 (April 1973).

4. Quoted in Dubos, *op. cit.,* p. 104.

5. *Ibid.,* p. 126.

6. Quoted in George Rosen, *From Medical Police to Social Medicine* (New York: Science History Publications, 1974), p. 62.

7. Dubos, *op. cit.,* p. 127; John Gordon Freymann, "Medicine's Great Schism: Prevention vs. Cure: An Historical Interpretation," *Medical Care* 13:525–36 (July 1975).

8. Powles, *op. cit.,* p. 15.

9. Dubos, *op. cit.,* p. 95.

10. Ibid., p. 71; Engel, op. cit., p. 131.
11. Powles, op. cit., p. 14.
12. Engel, op. cit., p. 132.
13. H. Jack Geiger, "The Illusion of Change," Social Policy 6(3): 30–35 at p. 33 (November/December 1975).
14. Eliot Freidson, Profession of Medicine: A Study of the Sociology of Applied Knowledge (New York: Dodd, Mead & Co., 1970), pp. 172–73.
15. Dubos, op. cit., p. 131.
16. Pharmaceutical Manufacturers Association, "A Prognosis for America," 1977, p. 3.
17. Rasmussen, op. cit., p. 56.
18. Halsted R. Holman, M.D., "A Matter of Standards: The 'Excellence' Deception in Medicine," speech to the Fourth Western Regional Conference on Rheumatic Diseases, December 5, 1975, p. 1. An abridged version of the speech is printed as an editorial, "The 'Excellence' Deception in Medicine," in Hospital Practice 11(4):11, 18, 21 (April 1976).
19. John H. Knowles, M.D., "The Hospital," Scientific American 229(3):128–37 at p. 135 (September 1973).
20. Holman, op. cit., p. 2.
21. Ibid., p. 4.
22. Raymond S. Duff and August B. Hollingshead, Sickness and Society (New York: Harper & Row, 1968), p. 8.
23. Robert H. Moser, "Psychosemantics (On Speaking to Patients)," in Robert H. Moser (ed.), Diseases of Medical Progress: A Study of Iatrogenic Disease (3d ed.) (Springfield: Charles C. Thomas, 1969), pp. 809–19 at pp. 809–10.
24. Richard M. Magraw, Ferment in Medicine: A Study of the Essence of Medical Practice and of Its New Dilemmas (Philadelphia: W. B. Saunders Co., 1966), pp. 140–41.
25. Duff and Hollingshead, op. cit., pp. 368–69. (Their study was of Yale-New Haven Hospital.)
26. Daniel Funkinstein, M.D., quoted in David Blumenthal and David Fallows, "Health: The Care We Want and Need," The Washington Monthly (October 1973), p. 14.
27. Quoted (anonymously) in Duff and Hollingshead, op. cit., p. 379.
28. Lewis Thomas (M.D.), "Rx for Illich" (a review of Ivan Illich, Medical Nemesis: The Expropriation of Health), The New York Review of Books, September 16, 1976, pp. 3–4 at p. 4.

29. Lewis Thomas, quoted in Henry Romney, "Doing Better and Feeling Worse, Some Dilemmas of American Doctors and Patients," *RF Illustrated* (a publication of the Rockefeller Foundation) 3(1):5 (July 4, 1976).

30. George L. Engel, "Too Little Science: The Paradox of Modern Medicine's Crisis," *The Pharos of Alpha Omega Alpha* 39: 127–31 at p. 129 (October 1976).

31. Horacio Fabrega, Jr., "The Position of Psychiatry in the Understanding of Human Disease," *Archives of General Psychiatry* 32:1501–12 at p. 1505 (December 1975).

32. See, e.g., Duff and Hollingshead, *op. cit.,* pp. 278–79. ("Can physicians treat disease in the perspective of patient and family realities, or are they capable of treating disease only in a more abstract sense? We have reason to state that patients and families, in spite of the difficulties for them, were far more desirous of treatment in this perspective than were physicians willing to provide it.")

33. *Ibid.,* p. 380.

34. Fabrega, "Ethnomedical Science," *op. cit.,* p. 973.

35. Engel, "New Medical Model," *op. cit.,* p. 135.

7 / The Commodification of Healing

1. Jerome D. Frank, "Mind-Body Relationships in Illness and Healing," *Journal of the International Academy of Preventive Medicine* II(3):46–59 at pp. 51–53 (Third Quarter 1975).

2. Adam Smith, "Here's to Our National Health," *New York* (January 17, 1977), p. 80.

3. Scott Greer, "Professional Self-Regulation in the Public Interest: The Intellectual Politics of PSRO [Professional Standards Review Organizations]," in *Proceedings: Conference on Professional Self-Regulation,* June 1975 (U.S. Department of Health, Education, and Welfare, Publication No. [HRA] 77–621), pp. 95–108 at p. 100.

4. Don E. Detmer and Helen H. Conrad, "Reflections upon Directive Language in Health Care," *Social Science and Medicine* 9:553–58 at p. 556 (October 1975). (Italics in the original.)

5. Clyde T. Hardy, Jr., "Medical Practice Today? It's Better Than Ever!", *Medical Economics* 52(27):64–67 (December 22, 1975); Karen A. Zupko, "If You Must Ask for Payment on the Spot, Here's How," *Medical Economics* 54(17):105–17 at

p. 108 (April 4, 1977); "The Growing Trend to Payment on the Spot," in "What's Ahead," *Medical Economics* 54(21):232 (October 17, 1977).

6. Lucia Fischer-Pap, "Has Success Spoiled Private Practice?", *Medical Dimensions* 6(5):27–30 at p. 28 (May 1977).

7. *Ibid.*, p. 29.

8. Greer, *op. cit.*, p. 99.

9. Barbara Myerhoff and William R. Larson, "The Doctor as Cultural Hero: The Routinization of Charisma," *Human Organization* 24:188–91 at p. 190 (Fall 1965).

10. Studs Terkel, *Working* (New York: Avon, 1975), p. 649. (Italics in the original.)

11. Halsted R. Holman, "A Matter of Standards: The 'Excellence' Deception in Medicine," speech to the Fourth Western Regional Conference on Rheumatic Diseases, December 5, 1975, p. 6. An abridged version of the speech is printed as an editorial, "The 'Excellence' Deception in Medicine," in *Hospital Practice* 11(4):11, 18, 21 (April 1976).

12. Mark G. Field, "The Health Care System of Industrial Society: The Disappearance of the General Practitioner and Some Implications," in Everett Mendelsohn, Judith P. Swazey, and Irene Taviss (eds.), *Human Aspects of Biomedical Innovation* (Cambridge: Harvard University Press, 1971), pp. 156–80 at p. 179.

13. Richard M. Titmuss, *The Gift Relationship* (New York: Pantheon Books, 1971), p. 170. ("We have been concerned to show the connections between the growth of commercial practices in certain sectors of medical care and the increasing application of the laws of the marketplace—of legalized and legitimated doctor-patient hostility. The second is a logical consequence of the first.")

14. Peter Singer, "Freedoms and Utilities in the Distribution of Health Care," in Robert M. Veatch and Roy Branson (eds.), *Ethics and Health Policy* (Cambridge, Mass.: Ballinger Publishing Co., 1976), pp. 175–93 at p. 179.

15. One doctor-participant in a panel on improving doctor-patient rapport even suggested that this was an appropriate stance: " 'We might improve our relationships a lot if we told patients that they are the *customers,* with as much right to complain about us as about a rude clerk or an inept plumber.' " "From Our Round Table: Improving Your One-to-One Patient Contacts," *Medical Economics* 53(25):21–28 at p. 28 (Novem-

ber 29, 1976), quoting Richard C. Bates, M.D., an internist practicing in Lansing, Michigan. (Italics in the original.)

8 / The Malpractice Crisis as Distortion

1. That official notice notably took the form of a 1969 report of a congressional subcommittee and a 1973 report of a commission created by the federal executive branch. Subcommittee on Executive Reorganization, Committee on Government Operations, U.S. Senate, *Medical Malpractice: The Patient Versus the Physician*, 91st Congress, 1st Session, Committee Print, 1969; *Report of the Secretary's Commission on Medical Malpractice* (Washington, D.C.: U.S. Department of Health, Education, and Welfare, 1973).
2. See, e.g., "Pricing Medical Malpractice Insurance: A Nontechnical Discussion of Ratemaking," in *Report of the Special Advisory Panel on Medical Malpractice, State of New York* (New York: The Panel, 1976), p. 216; Ian R. Heap, "The Liability Claims Explosion," *The Weekly Underwriter* 212(16):20–22 at p. 20 (April 26, 1975).
3. See, e.g., Richard S. L. Roddis and Richard E. Stewart, "The Insurance of Medical Losses," *Duke Law Journal* 1975:1281–1303 at pp. 1287–88 (January 1976).
4. "A Close Call," *Forbes* 117(8):30–36 at p. 30 (April 15, 1976).
5. Mark Kendall and John Haldi, "The Medical Malpractice Insurance Market," in *Appendix, Report of the Secretary's Commission, op. cit.*, Table III–7 at p. 510. At page 529, however, the authors couch their estimate as follows: "The total premium volume for physicians' and surgeons' professional liability insurance does not exceed 2.5 percent of the total property-liability insurance premium volume and may be somewhat less." That quote is echoed in the *Report* itself, at p. 41.
6. Dan R. Anderson, "Comments on Medical Malpractice Insurance—Face Up to the Problems of Cost," *Best's Review, Property/Liability Insurance Edition* 76(1):14–16, 82 at p. 16 (May 1975).
7. "A. M. Best Co. Comment on the State of and Prospects for the Property/Liability Insurance Industry," *Best's Review, Prop-*

erty/Liability Insurance Edition 76(2):10–12, 90–93 at p. 12 (June 1975).

8. Committee on Interstate and Foreign Commerce, U.S. House of Representatives, *National Conference on Medical Malpractice* (March 20–21, 1975), 94th Congress, 1st Session, Subcommittee Print, p. 12, transcribing remarks of Warren Cooper, Vice President and Actuary, Chubb & Son, Inc.

9. "Malpractice Insurance Outlook: Brightening," *Medical Economics* 48(16):103–28 at p. 110 (August 2, 1971), says, "Two decades ago . . ."; Committee on Medicine and Law, Association of the Bar of the City of New York, *Report on the Medical Malpractice Insurance Crisis* (New York: The Committee, 1975), p. 13 says, "Until about fifteen years ago . . ."

10. Kendall and Haldi, *op. cit.*, pp. 513, 531; Committee on Medicine and Law, *op. cit.*, p. 13.

11. Insurance Services Office, *Report to the All-Industry Committee, Special Malpractice Review: 1974 Closed Claim Survey, Preliminary Analysis of Survey Results* (New York: American Insurance Association, 1975), pp. 7, 24–30.

12. "Pricing Medical Malpractice Insurance," *op. cit.*, pp. 219–20.

13. Comment of Henry T. Kramer (President and Director, North American Reinsurance Corp. and a member of the HEW Secretary's Commission on Medical Malpractice), quoted in Kendall and Haldi, *op. cit.*, p. 523, n. 16.

14. "Answers to Additional Questions by Sen. Kennedy: Lester F. Senger, Vice President, Industry Affairs, Casualty & Surety Division, Aetna Life & Casualty Co.," *Hearings Before the Subcommittee on Health of the Committee on Labor and Public Welfare: Examination of the Continuing Medical Malpractice Insurance Crisis, 1975*, U.S. Senate, 94th Congress, 1st Session. Subcommittee Print, p. 325.

15. E. L. Calhoun (Assistant Vice President, CNA/Insurance Co.), "Professional Negligence: The Legal Responsibility of the Licensed Professional and the Current Trends of Consumerism" (excerpts of a speech to the American Management Association), *International Insurance Monitor* XXVI:416–20 at p. 420 (December 1972).

16. William J. Hazam, "Professional Negligence: Rate-Making Consideration for Doctors' Professional Liability," *International Insurance Monitor* XXVI:420–24 at p. 422 (December 1972); Roddis and Stewart, *op. cit.*, pp. 1295–96.

17. Robert B. Wilcox, "The Property/Liability Industry in Dis-

array: What Response?" (speech to the American Mutual Insurance Alliance Mutual Insurance Technical Conference), *The Weekly Underwriter* 213(2):16–17 at p. 17 (December 13, 1975).

18. *Report of the Secretary's Commission, op. cit.,* p. 3.

19. For general discussions of the data problem, see, e.g., Kendall and Haldi, *op. cit.,* pp. 533, 535; Buddy Steves, "Medical Malpractice in Perspective," *CPCU Annals* 28:209–23 at p. 213 (December 1975); *The Problems of Insuring Medical Malpractice* (New York: American Insurance Association, 1975), pp. 11–12; Robert N. Gilmore, Jr. (Senior Vice President for Legal Affairs, American Insurance Association), "Medical Malpractice—An Insurer's Perspective," address before the American College of Legal Medicine, May 14, 1976, pp. 1–2.

20. Kendall and Haldi, *op. cit.,* p. 533.

21. Gilmore, *op. cit.,* p. 4.

22. Steves, *op. cit.,* pp. 213–14.

23. *The Problems of Insuring Medical Malpractice, op. cit.,* p. 3.

24. "Data on Medical Malpractice in New York State," in *Report of the Special Advisory Panel, op. cit.,* p. 246, Table 5.

25. "Malpractice Insurance Outlook: Brightening," *op. cit.,* p. 104.

26. Kendall and Haldi, *op. cit.,* p. 494.

27. *Ibid.,* p. 549.

28. *Ibid.,* pp. 602–5.

29. *Ibid.,* p. 551.

30. "Malpractice Outlook," *op. cit.,* p. 118.

31. *Ibid.,* p. 119.

32. Kendall and Haldi, *op. cit.,* p. 518.

33. Lois J. Lyons, " 'Don't Blame Me' Everyone's Theme Song at N.Y. Hearing," *The National Underwriter* (February 14, 1975), p. 39, quoting testimony at a joint hearing of the New York State Assembly Committees on Health and Insurance of Alex Goldberger, liaison representative of the Greater New York Insurance Brokers Association.

34. "Medical Malpractice Insurance, Report of the NAIC Industry Advisory Committee," an edited version of a report submitted at the June 1972 meeting of the National Association of Insurance Commissioners, *Best's Review, Property/Liability Insurance Edition* 73(6):40–44, 78–84 at p. 42 (October 1972).

35. Kendall and Haldi, *op. cit.,* p. 511.

36. "Review and Preview," *Best's Review, Property/Liability Insurance Edition* 73(9):10–11, 91–94 at p. 10 (January 1973).

37. "A. M. Best Co. Comment," *op. cit.,* p. 90.
38. Figure for 1972: "Review and Preview," *op. cit.,* p. 11; for 1973: "Review and Preview," *Best's Review, Property/Liability Insurance Edition* 74(9):10–12, 95–98 at p. 11 (January 1974); for 1974: "Review and Preview," *Best's Review, Property/Liability Insurance Edition* 75(9):10–12, 74–78 at p. 11 (January 1975).
39. "The Case of the Contrary Curve," *Forbes* (February 15, 1976), p. 23.
40. Figures for 1973: "Review and Preview" of January 1974, *op. cit.,* p. 11; for 1974: "1974 Underwriting Results by Line of Business," *Best's Review, Property/Liability Insurance Edition* 76(1):10–12 at p. 12 (May 1975).
41. Robert J. Schraeder (Vice President, A. M. Best Co.), "Comment on the Need for the Exceptional Exercise of Management and Regulatory Responsibility in the Insurance Industry," *Best's Review, Property/Liability Insurance Edition* 75(11):12–18, 90 at p. 18 (March 1975).
42. *Ibid.,* p. 12.
43. Roddis and Stewart, *op. cit.,* pp. 1288–89.
44. "A. M. Best Co. Comment," *op. cit.,* p. 91.
45. T. Lawrence Jones (President, American Insurance Association), "Medical Malpractice Crisis: The 'Insurance Triangle' Is Upside Down," *The Weekly Underwriter* 213(11):10, 19–21 at p. 10 (September 20, 1975).
46. "Review and Preview," *Best's Review, Property/Liability Insurance Edition* 76(9):10–12, 64–71 at p. 70 (January 1976).
47. Barbara Yuncker, "The Malpractice Dispute: Doctors and Insurance," *New York Post,* January 11, 1975, p. 25.
48. Murray Teigh Bloom, "Malpractice: The Mess That Must Be Ended," *Reader's Digest* (April 1975), pp. 77–80.
49. *The Problems of Insuring Medical Malpractice, op. cit.,* p. 2.
50. Sources of information on the Argonaut saga are: "Prepared Statement of John Wadlewski, Vice President, Argonaut Insurance Company," *Hearings Before the Senate Subcommittee on Health, op. cit.,* pp. 158–62; Stephen J. Sansweet, "Teledyne Takes Drastic Steps in an Effort to Salvage Its Argonaut Insurance Unit," *The Wall Street Journal,* January 30, 1975; "Teledyne Says It Erred In Letting Unit Cover Medical Malpractice," *The Wall Street Journal,* February 19, 1975; "Teledyne Sees Threat to Insurance Unit's Solvency from Suits," *The Wall Street Journal,* April 4, 1975; Kendall and Haldi, *op. cit.,*

pp. 572–75; Robert Lindsey, "For Argonaut, Profits Proved Il-
lusory," *The New York Times*, June 8, 1975; Thomas F. Sheehan, *The Medical Malpractice Crisis in Insurance: How It Happened and Some Proposed Solutions*, a report prepared for the
American Bar Association, Section of Insurance, Negligence
and Compensation Law, Committee on Medical Malpractice,
for its Annual Meeting on August 12, 1975 (Chicago: The Association, 1975), p. 2; "Malpractice Rates: Up, Up, and
Away!", *Medical World News* (January 27, 1975), p. 24; "Malpractice Carrier Sails Away," *Medical World News* (March 24,
1975), pp. 23–25.
51. Sheehan, *op. cit.*, p. 24.
52. "Henry Singleton's Singular Conglomerate," *Forbes* 117(9):
38–39 at p. 39 (May 1, 1976).

9 / The Malpractice Debate
as Distortion

1. Linda Greenhouse, "'Must' Bills Add Urgency to Albany's
Closing Rush," *The New York Times*, May 10, 1976, p. 30.
2. Physicians Crisis Committee, *Court Docket Survey* (Detroit:
The Committee, 1975), foreword (unnumbered page).
3. Robert C. Strodel, J.D., "Piercing the Veil of Silence in Malpractice Litigation," presentation to Symposium on Socio-
Economic Problems of Internal Medicine in Illinois, Illinois
Society of Internal Medicine, April 4, 1975, reprinted in Association of Trial Lawyers of America, *Quality Medical Care—
The Citizen's Right* (Cambridge, Mass.: The Association,
1975), Vol. I, pp. 93–115 at p. 96. This three-volume anthology
of reports, position papers, testimony, and clippings is both a
useful, though limited, compendium and an illustration of how
the malpractice debate is distorted by vested interests. Its very
title, for example, misleads the reader either by implying that
the contents deal with something broader than the malpractice
crisis (they don't) or by implying that the problem of the quality of medical care is identical to the malpractice crisis. On the
inside, the distortions include a section that the table of contents bills as "The Medical Point of View" but that is liberally
sprinkled with reproductions of articles that are explicitly or
implicitly critical of the medical profession.
4. Lawyers Interested in Victim's Equity (LIVE), "Statement to

the Joint [New York State] Assembly [Insurance] and Health Committees on Medical Malpractice Legislation," January 31, 1975, reprinted in *ibid.*, Vol. I, pp. 326–30 at p. 328.

5. "Solution: 'Bridle the Lawyers!'," *Physician's Management* 15(8):35–49 at p. 35 (August 1975). See also Ester Gottlieb Smith and Paula Rogge, "The Malpractice Crisis: Views of Illinois Physicians," *Illinois Medical Journal* 150:79–85 at p. 81 (July 1976). ("More aggressive trial lawyers" was chosen as a cause of the increase in malpractice claims by 78 percent of the sample, while "less communication between doctor and patient" was chosen by 49 percent.)

6. Physicians Crisis Committee, *op. cit.*, p. 6.

7. Edward Edelson, "Doctors Blame Lawyers for Malpractice Crunch," New York *Daily News*, January 3, 1975, p. 36, quoting "one surgeon."

8. New York State Trial Lawyers Association, "Malpractice Suits, Patients' Only Protection, Should Not Be Outlawed," (undated) reprinted in Association of Trial Lawyers of America, *op. cit.*, pp. 294–307 at p. 305.

9. Letter of February 13, 1975, from Lindley M. Cowperthwait, Jr., President, Pennsylvania Trial Lawyers Association, to John G. McCullough, Editorial Page Editor, Philadelphia *Bulletin*, reprinted in *ibid.*, Vol. II, pp. 1159–60 at p. 1159.

10. San Francisco Trial Lawyers, "Malpractice Trial Lawyers' Reply," *Los Angeles Trial Lawyers Association Advocate* (March 1975), reprinted in *ibid.*, Vol. I, pp. 257–62 at p. 261.

11. David Bird, "3 Views on Malpractice: Doctor, Lawyer, Patient," *The New York Times*, April 23, 1975, quoting Charles Kramer, chairman of the New York State Trial Lawyers Association malpractice committee.

12. The so-called Waxman Committee Report, for example, citing testimony by a represenative of the California Trial Lawyers Association, reports that amount of probable damages as the threshold for "some malpractice specialists." California Assembly Select Committee on Medical Malpractice, *Preliminary Report*, June 1974, reprinted in Association of Trial Lawyers of America, *op. cit.*, Vol. I, pp. 128–229 at p. 177.

13. Robert E. Cartwright (Past President, Association of Trial Lawyers of America), "Medical Malpractice: A Trial Lawyer's View," in David G. Warren and Richard Merritt (eds.), *A Legislator's Guide to the Medical Malpractice Issue* (Washington,

D.C.: Health Policy Center and National Conference of State Legislatures, 1975), p. 61. (Italics in the original.)

14. Jack Werchick, "The Contingent Fee," in Association of Trial Lawyers of America, *op. cit.,* Vol. III, pp. 1363–66 at p. 1365.

15. Strodel, *op. cit.,* p. 96.

16. Cartwright, *op. cit.,* p. 61.

17. San Francisco Trial Lawyers, *op. cit.,* p. 258.

18. New York State Trial Lawyers Association, *op. cit.,* p. 299.

19. Ralph Emerson, M.D. (President, Medical Society of the State of New York), "Medical Malpractice Insurance: A Public Problem," advertising supplement to Sunday *New York Times,* April 11, 1976, p. 3.

20. A. Reynolds Crane, M.D. (President, Pennsylvania Medical Society), "Testimony, [Pennsylvania] Insurance Commission Hearings, March 18, 1975, Philadelphia," reprinted in Association of Trial Lawyers of America, *op. cit.,* Vol. I, pp. 560–67 at p. 560.

21. Committee on Interstate and Foreign Commerce, U.S. House of Representatives, *National Conference on Medical Malpractice* (March 20–21, 1975), 94th Congress, 1st Session, Subcommittee Print, p. 22, transcribing remarks of John J. Coury, M.D., Member, American Medical Association Council on Legislation.

22. Crane, *op. cit.,* p. 565.

23. Physicians Crisis Committee, *op. cit.,* p. 30.

24. See, e.g., *ibid.,* pp. 44, 45; Crane, *op. cit.,* pp. 566, 567.

10 / The Malpractice Crisis as Vicious Circle

1. Committee on Interstate and Foreign Commerce, U.S. House of Representatives, *National Conference on Medical Malpractice* (March 20–21, 1975), 94th Congress, 1st Session, Subcommittee Print, p. 24, transcribing remarks of Edward D. Henderson, M.D., Chairman of the Professional Services Committee of the American Academy of Orthopaedic Surgeons.

2. "Statement of George Northrup, D.O.," in *Report of the Secretary's Commission on Medical Malpractice* (Washington, D.C.: U.S. Department of Health, Education, and Welfare, 1973), pp. 105–8 at p. 106.

3. Eliot Freidson, *Profession of Medicine: A Study of the Sociology of Applied Knowledge* (New York: Dodd, Mead & Co., 1970), pp. 178–79.

4. Richard M. Magraw, *Ferment in Medicine: A Study of the Essence of Medical Practice and of Its New Dilemmas* (Philadelphia: W. B. Saunders Co., 1966), p. 73.

5. Howard M. Spiro, "The Kelly in the Belly—Some Comments on Malpractice," *New England Journal of Medicine* 296: 557–59 at p. 558 (March 10, 1977).

6. The National Association of Insurance Commissioners closed-claims study found that 92 percent of claims were settled or abandoned before trial, 3 percent were settled during trial, 1 percent were resolved by arbitration or review panels, and 4 percent were tried. Defendants won 80 percent of the cases tried; if these are combined with cases settled during trial, defendants won 72 percent. National Association of Insurance Commissioners, *Malpractice Claims No. 4* (Milwaukee: The Association, 1977), p. 94.

7. Howard Eisenberg, "Fresh Evidence on the Effects of the Malpractice Crisis," *Medical Economics* 54(8):79 (April 18, 1977).

8. Spiro, *op. cit.*, p. 558.

9. *Ibid.*, p. 557.

10. Marc J. Lane, *The Doctor's Lawyer: A Legal Handbook for Doctors* (Springfield, Ill.: Charles C. Thomas, 1974), p. 54.

11. Richard P. Bergen (J.D.), "Defensive Medicine Is Good Medicine," *Journal of the American Medical Association* 228: 1188–89 at p. 1189 (May 27, 1974).

12. A former Secretary of Health, Education, and Welfare used to claim that medical expenditures of $3 to $7 billion annually were going to defensive medicine, although how even such an amorphous estimate could be derived was never made clear. Caspar Weinberger, "Malpractice—A National View," *Arizona Medicine* 32:117–18 at p. 117 (February 1975).

13. Robert B. Sawyer, "My Opinion: One Eye on the Patient, the Other on the Courtroom," *American Medical News,* June 6, 1977, p. 20.

14. "Why Most MDs Practice 'Defensive Medicine,'" *American Medical News*, March 28, 1977, p. *Impact/3*.

15. Medical Society of Virginia, "Medical Malpractice Insurance Surveys," p. 3 (undated mimeo). This poll is reported in Eisenberg, *op. cit.*

16. Reported in Albert J. Lipson, *Medical Malpractice: The Response of Physicians to Premium Increases in California* (Santa Monica: The Rand Corporation, 1976), p. 52.
17. *Making Your Practice More Malpractice Proof* (Oradell, N.J.: Medical Economics Co. Book Division, 1975), pp. 4, 11.
18. "Preliminary Results from the Questionnaire on Professional Liability," *Bulletin of the American College of Surgeons* 57(5): 12–15 at p. 14 (May 1972). Those readers familiar with the literature on defensive medicine may be wondering why I have not cited the 1971 Duke Law School study, reported at "Project: The Medical Malpractice Threat: A Study of Defensive Medicine," *Duke Law Journal* 1971:939–93 (1971). The reason is simply that I find it impossible to take seriously an effort to survey anything related to the malpractice problem that excludes general surgeons and anesthesiologists from the physician population being surveyed.
19. *Making Your Practice More Malpractice Proof, op. cit.,* p. 32.
20. "Preliminary Results," *op. cit.,* p. 14.
21. *Making Your Practice More Malpractice Proof, op. cit.,* pp. 24–25.
22. *Ibid.,* pp. 26–27.
23. *Ibid.,* pp. 39–40.
24. "Preliminary Results," *op. cit.,* p. 14.
25. Medical Society of Virginia, *op. cit.,* p. 4.
26. Lipson, *op. cit.,* p. 54.
27. *Ibid.,* p. 62.
28. *Making Your Practice More Malpractice Proof, op. cit.,* pp. 29–31.
29. "Practice Management," *Medical Economics* 53(2):51 (January 26, 1976).
30. David S. Rubsamen, "Medical Malpractice," *Scientific American* 235(2):18–23 at pp. 21–22 (August 1976).
31. Nathan Hershey, "The Defensive Practice of Medicine—Myth or Reality?", *Milbank Memorial Fund Quarterly* 50:69–98 at p. 91 (January 1972).
32. *Making Your Practice More Malpractice Proof, op. cit.,* p. 12.
33. *Ibid.,* p. 29.
34. *Ibid.,* p. 5.
35. Michael E. Arnoff, "Putting the Patient Firmly on Your Side," *Medical Economics* 52(18):64–66 at p. 65 (September 1, 1975).

36. *Making Your Practice More Malpractice Proof, op. cit.,* p. 14. (Italics in the original.)
37. Letter to *The New York Times* from Drs. Robert Ebert, John Enders, and David Rutstein of Harvard Medical School, Dr. Thomas Chalmers of Mt. Sinai School of Medicine, Dr. Thomas Grayson of the University of Washington, and Dr. Abraham Lilienfeld of Johns Hopkins University, January 10, 1977, reprinted in part in *The Harvard Medical School Health Letter* II(5):6 (March 1977), with the introduction: "The following quote . . . expresses a sentiment that deserves wide understanding."
38. Quoted in Lipson, *op. cit.,* p. 52.

11 / The Futility of Official Responses

1. Report of the Board of Trustees. Subject: Professional Liability. Presented by: Raymond T. Holden, M.D., Chairman, American Medical Association Report H (C–76) (Chicago: The Association, 1976), pp. 1–2.
2. The number of states and territories is deduced from "Topical Summary of Recent Legislation Related to Medical Malpractice," in National Association of Insurance Commissioners, *Malpractice Claims No. 4* (Milwaukee: The Association, 1977), pp. 131–44 and American Medical Association Legislative Department, *State Health Legislation Report: A Special Update and Review on Medical Malpractice Legislation and Related Court Decisions* (Chicago: The Association, May 1977), pp. 26–27. The number of bills enacted comes from *ibid.,* p. 1 (approximately 102 in 1976) and Robert N. Gilmore, Jr., "Medical Malpractice—An Insurer's Perspective," speech before the American College of Legal Medicine, May 14, 1976, p. 6 (166 in 1975).
3. William J. Curran, "Malpractice Crisis: The Flood of Legislation," *New England Journal of Medicine* 293:1182–83 at p. 1182 (December 4, 1975).
4. William J. Curran, *How Lawyers Handle Medical Malpractice Cases* (U.S. Department of Health, Education, and Welfare, Publication No. [HRA] 76–3152), p. 34.
5. Assemblyman Barry Keene, "California's Medical Malpractice

Crisis," in David G. Warren and Richard Merritt (eds.), *A Legislator's Guide to the Medical Malpractice Issue* (Washington, D.C.: Health Policy Center, Georgetown University and National Conference of State Legislatures, 1975), pp. 27–34 at p. 32. (Italics in the original.)

6. This description of lobbying activity is drawn from reports to the AMA by the staffs of state medical societies, compiled in American Medical Association Staff Task Force on Professional Liability, *State-by-State Report on the Professional Liability Issue* (Chicago: The Association, 1976).

7. Keene, *op. cit.,* p. 33.

8. Rep. Joseph C. Czerwinski, "Wisconsin's Medical Malpractice Crisis," in Warren and Merritt, *op. cit.,* pp. 49–58 at p. 49.

9. AMA Staff Task Force on Professional Liability, *op. cit.,* p. 1 under "California."

10. David M. Kinzer, "Laws on Order: Confessions of a Lobbyist," *Modern Hospital* 117:139–58 at p. 140 (September 1971).

11. National Conference of State Legislatures, *Medical Malpractice and the State Legislatures* (Denver: The Conference, April 1976), p. 6.

12. The description of JUA's draws on Gilmore, *op. cit.,* p. 607; Curran, "Law-Medicine Notes," *op. cit.,* p. 1183; Warren and Merrit, *op. cit.,* pp. 4–6; AMA Legislative Department, *op. cit.,* pp. 10–11; National Association of Insurance Commissioners, *op. cit.,* pp. 131–32.

13. *Report of the Special Advisory Panel on Medical Malpractice, State of New York* (New York: The Panel, 1976), p. 124.

14. AMA Legislative Department, *op. cit.,* p. 11.

15. Gilmore, *op. cit.,* p. 7.

16. *Ibid.,* pp. 7–8; AMA Legislative Department, *op. cit.,* pp. 14–15; Warren and Merritt, *op. cit.,* p. 6; National Association of Insurance Commissioners, *op. cit.,* pp. 132–33.

17. AMA Legislative Department, *op. cit.,* pp. 3–4; American Bar Association Fund for Public Education, *Legal Topics Relating to Medical Malpractice* (U.S. Department of Health, Education, and Welfare, 1977), pp. 8–10.

18. *Wright v. Central Du Page Hospital Assn.,* 347 N.E.2d 736 (Ill. 1976), described in AMA Legislative Department, *op. cit.,* p. 19.

19. Described *ibid.,* pp. 18–20; ABA Fund for Public Education, *op. cit.,* pp. 66–67.

20. Curran, *How Lawyers Handle, op. cit.,* p. 36.
21. National Association of Insurance Commissioners, *op. cit.,* p. 101, Table 23.
22. Curran, *How Lawyers Handle, op. cit.,* p. 36.
23. AMA Legislative Department, *op. cit.,* p. 4; National Association of Insurance Commissioners, *op. cit.,* p. 135; Warren and Merritt, *op. cit.,* p. 9; "An Analysis of State Legislative Responses to the Medical Malpractice Crisis," *Duke Law Journal* 1975:1417–68 at pp. 1447–50.
24. *Graley v. Satayatham,* 343 N.E.2d 832 (Court of Common Pleas of Cuyahoga County, Ohio, 1976), described in ABA Fund for Public Education, *op. cit.,* p. 65.
25. *Ibid.,* p. 64.
26. National Association of Insurance Commissioners, *op. cit.,* p. 134; "Analysis of State Legislative Responses," *op. cit.,* pp. 1442–46.
27. *Byrne v. Boadle,* 159 Eng. Rep. 299 (Court of Exchequer Chamber, 1863). ("There are certain cases of which it may be said *res ipsa loquitur* and this seems one of them.")
28. ABA Fund for Public Education, *op. cit.,* p. 15; Curran, *How Lawyers Handle, op. cit.,* p. 39.
29. "Analysis of State Legislative Responses," *op. cit.,* pp. 1436–42; ABA Fund for Public Education, *op. cit.,* pp. 13–14; Curran, *How Lawyers Handle, op. cit.,* p. 38.
30. National Association of Insurance Commissioners, *op. cit.,* pp. 92–93. (The report does not indicate what percentage of claims raised the issue.)
31. AMA Legislative Department, *op. cit.,* p. 2; ABA Fund for Public Education, *op. cit.,* p. 13; National Association of Insurance Commissioners, *op. cit.,* pp. 133–34.
32. "Analysis of State Legislative Responses," *op. cit.,* pp. 1429–36; AMA Legislative Department, *op. cit.,* p. 2; ABA Fund for Public Education, *op. cit.,* pp. 10–12; National Association of Insurance Commissioners, *op. cit.,* pp. 139–40.
33. New York State Special Advisory Panel, *op. cit.,* p. 176.
34. National Association of Insurance Commissioners, *op. cit.,* p. 17, Table 1a, 2a.
35. "Analysis of State Legislative Responses," *op. cit.,* pp. 1456–63; AMA Legislative Department, *op. cit.,* pp. 17–18; National Association of Insurance Commissioners, *op. cit.,* pp. 137–38; Curran, *How Lawyers Handle, op. cit.,* pp. 39–41; ABA Fund For Public Education, *op. cit.,* pp. 2–3, 49–52.

36. New York State Special Advisory Panel, *op. cit.*, p. 165.
37. *Ibid.*, p. 210.
38. *Ibid.*, p. 211.
39. Irving Ladimer and Joel Solomon, "Medical Malpractice Arbitration: Law, Programs, Cases," *Insurance Law Journal* 653: 335–65 at pp. 337–38 (June 1977).
40. *Ibid.*, pp. 341–47.
41. Richard L. Peck, "Binding Malpractice Arbitration: Most Doctors Are for It," *Medical Economics* 54(7):135–40 (April 4, 1977); Sheridan and Ferber, *op. cit.*, p. 86; Curran, "Malpractice Arbitration," *op. cit.*, p. 1045; "Malpractice Problems and Proposed Solutions Discussed by Hospital Attorneys at Annual Meeting," *Hospitals* 50(13):17–17c (July 1, 1976).
42. Brenda Stone, "After 50 Years—Still Too Soon to Judge Worth of Arbitration," *American Medical News,* May 9, 1977, pp. 7–8 at p. 8, reporting on a national conference on malpractice arbitration sponsored by the American Arbitration Association and the American College of Legal Medicine.
43. National Association of Insurance Commissioners, *op. cit.*, p. 94.
44. Stone, *op. cit.*, reporting an American Arbitration Association study of 55 cases of completed arbitration (45 percent awarding damages), a Kaiser Foundation Health Plan study of 14 cases (70 percent), and a Suffolk County, New York, study of 19 cases (47 percent).
45. Ladimer and Solomon, *op. cit.*, p. 355.
46. *Ibid.*, pp. 356–67, for example, make the argument that arbitration is cheaper and speedier than litigation; ABA Fund for Public Education, *op. cit.*, p. 40 casts doubt on that argument.
47. National Association of Insurance Commissioners, *op. cit.*, p. 94 (92 percent abandoned or settled before trial, 3 percent settled during trial, 1 percent resolved by review panels or arbitration, and 4 percent tried).
48. Warren and Merritt, *op. cit.*, p. 7; ABA Fund for Public Education, *op. cit.*, p. 4; Robert H. Brook, Rudolf L. Brutoco, and Kathleen N. Williams, "The Relationship Between Medical Malpractice and Quality of Care," *Duke Law Journal* 1975:1197–1232 at pp. 1224–25 (1976).
49. AMA Legislative Department, *op. cit.*, p. 13; Brook et al., *op. cit.*, pp. 1223–24.
50. New York State Consumer Protection Board, *Rights Without Remedies: A Study of Complaint Handling Mechanisms in Pro-*

fessional Misconduct Cases in New York State (Albany: The Board, 1977), pp. 3, 24, 4.

51. New York State Assembly Standing Committee on Health and Standing Committee on Insurance, *First Interim Report on Medical Practice Problems in the State of New York* (Albany: The New York State Assembly, 1977), pp. 2–3, 5–6.

52. "When Malpractice Defendants Don't Bite the Bullet," in "Professional Briefs," *Medical Economics* 54(17):11–12 at p. 12 (August 22, 1977).

53. Tom Stevenson, "Captive Insurance—Risk Replaces Premiums," *The New York Times*, Sunday, May 29, 1977, Sec. 3, p. 1.

54. Emily Friedman, "Hospital Insurance Captives: Their Time Has Come," *Hospitals* 51(6):84–88 at p. 88 (March 16, 1977).

55. *Ibid.*, p. 84; AMA Legislative Department, *op. cit.*, p. 11.

56. Carol Brierly Golin, "Harvard's Offshore Captive Plan," *American Medical News*, July 26, 1976, p. *Impact/*7; "Grand Cayman Insurance," *Health Lawyers News Report* 4(4):7 (April 1976).

57. "Judge Restrains Insurance Commissioner," *MLC* [Medical Liability Commission] *Commentary* 3(8):3 (August 1976).

58. "Minnesota Plans Offshore Captive Insurance Co.," *Hospitals* 51(1):22–23 (January 1, 1977).

59. Friedman, *op. cit.*, p. 88.

60. Philip Harsham, "Offshore Malpractice Insurance: Is It the Answer for You?", *Medical Economics* 54(3):214–26 at pp. 218, 221, 222 (February 7, 1977).

61. "Doctor-Owned Insurance Companies: How They Are Faring," *Medical World News* 17(18):17–18 at p. 17 (August 23, 1976).

62. "Special Report: Why the Malpractice Crisis Has to Get Worse to Get Better," *Medical Economics* 54(2):37–50 at pp. 41–42, interviewing Eli P. Bernzweig.

63. Friedman, *op. cit.*, pp. 84, 86.

64. Priscilla S. Meyer, "Medical Malpractice Insurance Crisis May End Up Improving Hospital Care," *The Wall Street Journal*, December 27, 1976, p. 2.

65. An American Hospital Association mailing dated October 1976 announced "a new publication: *Controlling Hospital Liability: A Systems Approach*"; an undated mailing from the Federation of American Hospitals (apparently prepared in the summer of 1977) announced publication of a *Risk Management Manual*.

66. Thomas S. Chittenden, "Risk Management: Role of Physician in Malpractice Needs More Careful Exploration," *Hospitals* 51(1):53–56 at p. 53 (May 16, 1977); Herman M. Somers, "The Malpractice Controversy and the Quality of Patient Care," *Health and Society/Milbank Memorial Fund Quarterly* 55:193–232 at p. 227 (Spring 1977).

67. AMA Legislative Department, *op. cit.,* pp. 15–16, 25.

68. Chittenden, *op. cit.,* pp. 53, 54.

69. "Malpractice '77: 50-State Picture Improves," *Medical World News* 18(1):21–23 (January 10, 1977); see also ABA Fund for Public Education, *op. cit.,* pp. 72–73.

12 / The Dilemmas of Reform

1. Sidney M. Wolfe, "Medical Malpractice: A Consumer Representative's View," in David G. Warren and Richard Merritt (eds.), *A Legislator's Guide to the Medical Malpractice Issue* (Washington, D.C.: Health Policy Center, Georgetown University and National Conference of State Legislatures, 1975), pp. 73–75 at pp. 73, 74.

2. Robert E. McGarrah, Jr., "How Can I Find a Good Doctor?", *Health Law Project Library Bulletin* 322:1–5 at p. 2 (June 1976); Herbert S. Denenberg, *A Shopper's Guide to Surgery: Fourteen Rules on How to Avoid Unnecessary Surgery,* a booklet "reprinted by Blue Cross" (1972).

3. Priscilla Laws, *Medical and Dental X-Rays: A Consumer's Guide to Avoiding Unnecessary Radiation Exposure* (Washington, D.C.: Public Citizen's Health Research Group, 1974).

4. McGarrah, *op. cit.,* p. 2.

5. "Court OKs Directory," *Health Lawyers News Report* 4(12):3 (December 1976).

6. "Advertising by Physicians," *Health Law Project Library Bulletin* 322:6 (June 1976); "AMA on Advertising," *Health Lawyers News Report* 4(7):3 (July 1976).

7. John Carlova, "What Would It Take to Make You Advertise?", *Medical Economics* 53(14):77–81 at p. 78 (July 12, 1976).

8. "Doctors Start Their Own Directories," *Medical World News* 18(17):37 (August 22, 1977).

9. McGarrah, *op. cit.,* pp. 2, 4.

10. See, e.g., Dennis Helfman et al., "Access to Medical Records," in *Appendix, Report of the Secretary's Commission on Medical*

Malpractice (Washington, D.C.: U.S. Department of Health, Education, and Welfare, 1973), pp. 177–213 (legalities); Carol A. Soskis, "Patients' Access to Their Medical Records: The Current Situation," *Health Law Project Library Bulletin* 326: 1–7 (November 1976) (legalities and practicalities). A particularly blatant disregard of legalities, in which a patient's bill of rights published for its patients by Beth Israel Hospital in Boston neglected to mention that Massachusetts law grants hospital patients the right to see and copy their medical records because the hospital's director disagreed with the law, is described in George Annas, "Voluntary and Regulatory Bills of Patients' Rights," in *Proceedings, National Symposium on Patients' Rights in Health Care*, May 17–18, 1976 (U.S. Department of Health, Education, and Welfare, Publication No. [HSA] 76–7002), pp. 13–16 at p. 15.

11. The symposium reported in *Proceedings, ibid.,* for example, is striking for the frequency with which concern about the problem of gaining access is expressed.

12. "Giving the Patient His Medical Record: A Proposal to Improve the System," *New England Journal of Medicine* 289: 688–92 (September 27, 1973).

13. *Ibid.,* p. 688.

14. "AMA Fights Ruling," *Health Lawyers News Report* 4(2):3 (February 1976); James A. Reynolds, "How Soon Will Your Colleagues Begin Advertising?", *Medical Economics* 53:31–40 at pp. 31–33 (February 23, 1976).

15. Michael Pertschuk, "Not At Any Price," remarks delivered at the Conference on "Competition in the Health Care Sector: Past, Present, and Future," sponsored by the FTC Bureau of Economics, June 1–2, 1977, p. 3.

16. Quoted in A. J. Vogel, "Is This What the F.T.C. Really Wants?", *Medical Economics* 54(4):82–89 at p. 85 (February 21, 1977).

17. Jerome D. Frank, *Persuasion and Healing* (rev. ed.) (New York: Schocken Books, 1974), p. 47. (The complete sentence is: "In contrast with scientific medicine which, while paying copious lip service to the doctor-patient relationship, in actuality largely ignores it, all nonmedical healing methods attach great importance to it.")

18. Shenkin and Warner, *op. cit.,* p. 689.

19. "Malpractice! A Consumer View," *Health Perspectives* 2(3): 1–7 at p. 6 (May–June 1975).

20. "The Self-Care Surge," *Medical World News* 18(20):43–54 at p. 43 (October 3, 1977).

21. Tom Ferguson, "The Self-Care Concept," *Medical Self-Care* II(1):4–5 at p. 4 (Spring 1977).

22. Randy Smith, "A Pound of Prevention," *Medical Dimensions* 6(1):24–29 at p. 24 (January 1977).

23. Lowell S. Levin, "Self-Care: An International Perspective," *Social Policy* 7(2):70–75 at p. 72 (September/October 1976).

24. Lowell S. Levin, Alfred H. Katz, and Erik Holst, *Self-Care: Lay Initiatives in Health* (New York: PRODIST, 1976), p. 27.

25. *Ibid.,* p. 24.

26. *Ibid.,* p. 34.

27. Sheryl K. Ruzek, "Emergent Modes of Utilization: Gynecological Self-Help," in Virginia Olesen (ed.), *Women and Their Health: Research Implications for a New Era* (U.S. Department of Health, Education, and Welfare, Publication No. [HRA] 77–3138), pp. 80–84 at p. 81; Helen I. Marieskind, "Helping Oneself to Health," *Social Policy* 7(2):63–66 at p. 64 (September/October 1976).

28. Boston Women's Health Book Collective, *Our Bodies, Ourselves* (2d ed.) (New York: Simon & Schuster, 1976), p. 367, quoting from an unidentified publication of the Women's Community Health Center in Cambridge, Massachusetts.

29. Marieskind, *op. cit.,* p. 66.

30. Ruzek, *op. cit.,* p. 82.

31. *Ibid.,* p. 81.

32. Various items in Vol. 1, Nos. 2 and 3 of the *Self-Help Reporter* (March/April and May/June 1977).

33. Alan Gartner and Frank Riessman, "Health Care in a Technological Age," in *Self-Help and Health: A Report* (New York: New Human Services Institute, 1976), pp. 27, 28, 29; H. Carson Briggs, "Conference on Self-Help and Health: Summary of Discussion," in *Self-Help and Health, op. cit.,* pp. 1–16 at p. 15.

34. Gartner and Riessman, *op. cit.,* pp. 27–32; Alan Gartner and Frank Riessman, "Self-Help Models and Consumer Intensive Health Practice," *American Journal of Public Health* 66:780–86 at p. 784 (August 1976).

35. Victor W. Sidel and Ruth Sidel, "Beyond Coping," *Social Policy* 7(2):67–69 at p. 67 (September/October 1976).

36. Gartner and Riessman in *American Journal of Public Health, op. cit.,* p. 784.

37. *Ibid.,* p. 785.

38. Bill Claflin and Pat Thaler, "Banding Together: The Best Way to Cope," *New York* (February 28, 1977), pp. 41–48 at p. 42.

39. Michael J. Kleeman and Janet L. DePree, "Self-Help Groups and Their Effectiveness as Agents for Chronic Illness Care: The Case of Kidney Transplant Patients," in *Self-Help and Health, op. cit.,* pp. 69–76 at p. 71.

40. Briggs, *op. cit.,* pp. 4, 16.

41. Boston Women's Health Book Collective, *op. cit.,* p. 12.

42. Marieskind, *op. cit.,* p. 65.

43. Stephen F. Jencks, "Problems in Participatory Health Care," in *Self-Help and Health, op. cit.,* pp. 85–98 at pp. 93–94.

44. Tom Dewar, "Professionalized Clients as Self-Helpers," in *Self-Help and Health, op. cit.,* pp. 77–84 at p. 80.

45. Frank, *op. cit.,* pp. 276, 278, 282.

46. See, e.g., Gartner and Riessman in *American Journal of Public Health, op. cit.,* p. 784 (". . . the helper in attempting to change or help the helpee becomes involved in persuading himself or herself [e.g., not to be alcoholic] while in the process of convincing the other.")

47. Sidel and Sidel, *op. cit.,* p. 68.

48. Jencks, *op. cit.,* pp. 94–95.

49. On the mammography muddle, see, e.g., Philip M. Hosay, "The Unfulfilled Promise of Health Education," *New York University Education Quarterly* VIII(2):16–22 at pp. 19–20. On the possible fallaciousness of the theory that reducing blood cholesterol levels will prevent heart attacks, see, e.g., Halsted R. Holman, "A Matter of Standards: The 'Excellence' Deception in Medicine," speech to the Fourth Western Regional Conference on Rheumatic Diseases, December 5, 1975, pp. 4–5, published in abridged form as an editorial, "The 'Excellence' Deception in Medicine," in *Hospital Practice* 11(4):11, 18, 21 (April 1976).

50. Barry Kramer, "The Future Revised: Wiser Way of Living, Not Dramatic 'Cures,' Seen as Key to Health," *The Wall Street Journal,* March 22, 1976, pp. 1, 19 at p. 1.

51. Henry M. Wriston, "Health Insurance," *The New York Times,* Sunday, May 23, 1976, Sec. 4, p. 17. (Italics in the original.)

52. Advertisement in, among other newspapers and other dates, *The New York Times,* June 15, 1977, p. A21.

53. Quoted from various of the unnumbered pages of the booklet *Get the Life That's Coming to You,* published by Blue Cross and Blue Shield of Greater New York, undated.

54. Robert M. Gibson and Marjorie Smith Mueller, "National Health Expenditures, Fiscal Year 1976," *Social Security Bulletin* 40(4):3–22 at p. 4, Chart 1 (April 1977).

55. *Consumer Health Education: A Directory, 1976* (U.S. Department of Health, Education, and Welfare, Publication No. [HRA] 77–607), p. iii.

56. Sally Guttmacher, "A Critique of Self-Help and Self-Care," *Self-Help Reporter* 1(3):6–7 at p. 6 (May/June 1977).

57. Boston Women's Health Book Collective, *op. cit.*, pp. 98–99.

58. In a fascinating book in which a doctor and a patient alternate their differing perceptions of the same medical crisis, the patient-author at one point reflects: "Despite intellectual objections that I or anyone else may have toward the medical profession, being seriously ill provides an emotional equalizer. Throughout my carping and complaining to Halberstam and the rest of the medical staff, I was, in reality, totally dependent on them. The knowledge of that dependency may well have been the source of much of my irritability. But the truth was that in quiet moments alone I repeated mental entreaties to Halberstam to save me, make me well, make me whole again." Michael Halberstam, M.D., and Stephan Lesher, *A Coronary Event* (Philadelphia and New York: J. B. Lippincott Company, 1976), p. 148.

59. Levin et al., *op. cit.*, p. 37.

60. The classic formulation of the need for different doctor-patient models to reflect different sickness situations is Thomas S. Szasz and Marc H. Hollender, "A Contribution to the Philosophy of Medicine: The Basic Models of the Doctor-Patient Relationship," *AMA Archives of Internal Medicine* 97:585–91 (May 1956). The concept of the doctor as assuming a leadership role is developed in John C. Whitehorn, "The Doctor's Image of Man," pp. 3–40 in Iago Galdston (ed.), *Man's Image in Medicine and Anthropology* (New York: International Universities Press, 1963).

Index

The numbers in brackets are note numbers. They indicate that the individual named is quoted or drawn on in the text but is identified only in the notes. For example, the entry "Abel-Smith, Brian, 73 [11] [12]" indicates that the quotation on page 73 followed by the superior number 11 is from a work by Brian Abel-Smith and that the statement on page 73 followed by the superior number 12 draws on his work.

Abel-Smith, Brian, 73 [11] [12], 213
Abernathy, William J., 40 [20]
ad damnum clause, 155–56
Aetna Life & Casualty Insurance Company, 109
Alcoholics Anonymous, 181
allied health personnel, 61–62
American Arbitration Association, 231
American Cancer Society, 100
American College of Surgeons, 136, 138
American Hospital Association, 164, 166
American Insurance Association, 108, 112, 117
American Medical Association, 134, 135, 143, 144, 164, 171–72, 173, 175, 176
anger of patients, 4–5, 6–10, 14, 31–33, 55–56, 65–67, 76–77, 90–91, 99–100, 140–42
Annas, George, 172 [10]
antibiotics, 29, 39, 45, 46, 49, 52
arbitration, 158–60
Argonaut Insurance Company, 118–20
Arnoff, Michael E., 131
Association of Trial Lawyers of America, 123 [3]

bad-apple theory, 129–30, 164, 176
Balint, Michael, 64 [29]
Barr, D. P., 45 [41]
Bates, Richard C., 218–29
Beeson, Paul B., 39 [13], 58 [5], 59 [7]
Bennett, John V., 30 [43]
Bergen, Richard P., 134 [11]
Berlin, Leonard, 3
Bernzweig, Eli, 3, 8 [8], 165 [62]

Best's Review, 116, 117
biomedical model, 79–91, 99, 169, 176, 184, 187, 188
biomedical research, see medical research
blaming the victim, 176–77, 184–87, 188–89
Blue Cross, 185–86
Blue Shield, 73, 185–86
Blum, Richard H., 7 [7], 9 [15], 12 [23], 14 [28], 20 [17], 21 [21], 33 [60], 53 [81], 67 [43], 76 [21], 195
Bolande, Robert P., 51 [71]
Boston Collaborative Drug Surveillance Program, 47
Boston Women's Health Book Collective, 179 [28], 182 [41], 187 [57]
Briggs, H. Carson, 180 [33], 181 [40]
Brook, Robert H., 162 [48] [49]
Brown, Esther Lucille, 20 [17], 66 [38]
Bunker, John P., 38 [12]
Burgess, Alex M., 37 [7]
Burgess, Alex M., Jr., 37 [7]
Burling, Temple, 24 [28], 59–60 [11], 63 [26], 199
Burrough, Bonnie, 63 [27]
Burrough, Vern, 63 [27]

Calhoun, E. L., 110 [15]
California Medical Association, 136, 145
Caranasos, George J., 48 [52] [53] [54], 65 [32]
Carlson, Rick J., 59 [9]
Cartwright, Frederick F., 51 [69]
Cartwright, Robert E., 121, 126 [13], 127 [16]
Child, Charles G. III, 50 [63]

Chittenden, Thomas S., 166 [66] [68]
Chubb & Son, Inc., 107
clinical laboratories, 36–37
clinical laboratory personnel, 61, 211
CNA/Insurance, 110
collateral source rule, 151–52
commodification, 92–100, 174–77, 187–89
Conrad, Helen H., xii [1], 95 [4]
Consumer Commission on the Accreditation of Health Services, 177
consumerism, medical, *see* medical consumerism
contingent fee, 124–26, 152
Controlled Risk Insurance Company, Ltd., 164–65
Cook, Fred J., 212
Cooper, Warren, 107 [8], 121
Coser, Rose Laub, 16, 19 [11] [16], 20 [17]
Coury, John J., 127 [21]
Cowperthwait, Lindley M., 125 [9]
Crane, A. Reynolds, 127 [20], 127–28 [22], 130 [24]
Curran, William J., 143 [3], 144 [4], 146 [12], 150 [20] [22], 154 [28], 155 [29], 157 [35]
Czerwinski, Joseph C., 145 [8]

Darwin, Charles, 80
defensive medicine, 133–42
Denenberg, Herbert, 170, 177
DePree, Janet L., 181 [39]
Detmer, Don E., xii [1], 95 [4]
Dewar, Robert, 20 [17], 21 [20]
Dewar, Tom, 182 [44]
Dichter, Ernest, 31 [52] [53], 66 [40]
dicoumarol, 40–41
doctor-patient relationship, 4, 11–15, 17, 21, 26–27, 36, 49–50, 54–56, 63–67, 69, 75–77, 86–87, 88–91, 93–95, 96, 98, 133–34, 135, 140–42, 175–76, 188–89, 195–96
doctors' directories, 171–72, 173, 174
doctrine of specific etiology, 79, 81
Donaldson, William F., 25 [30]
Dornette, William H. L., 30 [46]
drugs, 44–50, 64–65, 71, 84–85, 89, 94, 97, 207; *see also* antibiotics, medication error
Dubos, René, 79 [1], 80 [3], 81 [4] [5], 82, 84 [15]
Duff, Raymond S., 16, 19 [12] [13], 21 [18], 22 [24], 24 [27], 31 [52] [53], 32 [58], 53 [80], 55 [89] [90], 64 [30] [31], 87 [22] [25], 88 [27], 90 [33], 198, 200, 202, 217
Duke University Law School, 227

Ebert, Richard V., 53 [78]
Ebert, Robert H., 59 [8]
Eckenhoff, James E., 50 [62], 209
Egeberg, Roger, 55 [87]
Elman, Robert, 54 [84]
Emerson, Ralph, 127 [19]
Engel, George L., 79 [1], 80 [2], 82 [10], 83 [12], 88 [30], 90–91 [35]
Eyer, Joseph, 204

Fabrega, Horacio, Jr., 79 [1], 90 [31] [34]
Federal Trade Commission, 173–74
Federation of American Hospitals, 166
fee-for-service, 69, 70–71, 72, 74, 76–77, 84, 134
Feminist Women's Health Centers, 180
Ferguson, Tom, 178, 178 [21]
Field, Mark G., 65 [33], 67 [37], 67 [42], 99 [12]
financing of medical treatment, 68–77, 83–84, 162
Fischer-Pap, Lucia, 96 [6] [7]
Fisher, William C., 45 [41]
Freidson, Eliot, 72 [8], 73–74 [15], 84 [14], 92, 132 [3]
Friedman, Milton, 175
Fox, Maurice, 70 [5]
Fox, Renée C., 18 [9]
Frank, Jerome D., 49 [56], 93 [1], 175 [17], 182 [45]
Freymann, John Gordon, 81 [7]
Fuchs, Victor, 38 [8] [9]
Funkinstein, Daniel, 87–88 [26]

Gallagher, Eugene B., 66 [39]
Gartner, Alan, 180 [33], 181 [34] [36] [37], 183 [46]
gastric freezing, 41
Geiger, H. Jack, 83 [13]
Gemmill, Paul F., 214
germ theory of disease, 79–82
Gerson, Elihu M., 12 [21], 65 [34]
Gibson, Robert M., 39 [15], 186 [54]
Gilmore, Robert N., Jr., 111 [19], 112 [21], 143 [2], 146 [12], 149 [15]
Glaser, William A., 23 [25], 214
Goddard, James L., 41 [25]
Greer, Scott, 94 [3], 96 [8]
Guttmacher, Sally, 186 [56]

Halberstam, Michael, 237
Haldi, John, 106 [5], 107 [10], 111 [19], 112 [20], 114 [26] [27] [28], 114–15 [29], 115 [32], 116 [35], 118 [50], 219
Hall, William, 47 [48]

Handler, Seymour, 37 [6], 49 [57], 208

Harvard Medical School Health Letter, 228

Harvard University, 164

Harvard University Medical School, 87

healing, 11, 66, 92–94, 96, 184, 188

Health, Education, and Welfare, U.S. Department of, 186; *see also* Secretary's Commission on Medical Malpractice

health insurance, 18, 69, 72–74, 84, 95, 98–99

Health Research Group, 170, 171, 172

Helfman, Dennis, 172 [10]

Henderson, Edward D., 131 [1]

Hershey, Nathan, 139 [31]

Hess, Richard J., 40 [21], 42 [29], 43 [30] [31]

Hiatt, Howard H., 41 [23] [24], 53 [78]

Hollender, Marc H., 13 [26], 50 [58], 54 [85], 237

Hollingshead, August B., 16, 19 [12] [13], 21 [18], 22 [24], 24 [27], 31 [52] [53], 32 [58], 53 [80], 55 [89] [90], 64 [30] [31], 87 [22] [25], 88 [27], 90 [33], 198, 200, 202, 217

Holman, Halsted R., 85 [18], 86 [20] [21], 99 [11], 236

Hosay, Philip M., 236

hospital-acquired infection, *see* nosocomial infection

Hospital Association of Risk Managers, 166

hospital employees, 61–62

hospitals, 11, 16–33, 53–54, 61–62, 65–66, 75, 85–87, 89, 97, 98–99, 197, 198–99, 200; communications in, 25–26, 31–33; lines of authority in, 22–23; and defensive medicine, 138–40; and malpractice insurance, 106, 164–66; and risk management, 166; teaching hospitals, 19, 22, 39, 59, 64, 66, 82, 85–86, 87

Houston, Charles S., 31 [52]

Huntley, R. R., 48 [51]

hyperbaric chambers, 41

iatrogenic illness, 42, 43, 45–48, 51–52, 64–65, 139; *see also* injury, medical; medication error; nosocomial infection

ideology, 78–91, 99, 188–89

informed consent, 154–55

Ingelfinger, Franz J., 50 [60]

injury, medical, 4–6, 43, 45, 47–48, 51–52, 64–65, 139, 193–94; *see also* medication error, nosocomial infection

insurance, *see* health insurance, malpractice insurance

Insurance Services Office, 51 [67], 108–9 [11], 111–12, 197, 207

Jacobs, Bernard, 35 [1]

Janis, Irving L., 53–54 [82]

Jencks, Stephen F., 182 [43], 183–84 [48], 200

Jick, Hershel, 45 [41], 47 [49]

joint underwriting associations, 146–48, 167

Jones, T. Lawrence, 117 [45]

Jonsson, Egon, 53 [78]

Kaiser Foundation Health Plan, 231

Katz, Fred E., 60 [13]

Keene, Barry, 144 [5], 145 [7]

Kendall, Mark, 106 [5], 107 [10], 111 [19], 112 [20], 114 [26] [27] [28], 114–15 [29], 115 [32], 116 [35], 118 [50], 219

Kinzer, David M., 143, 146 [10]

Klarman, Herbert E., 73 [18]

Kleeman, Michael J., 181 [39]

Knowles, John H., 17 [5], 18 [10], 85–86 [19], 185

Koch, Robert, 80, 82

Korsch, Barbara M., 196

Kramer, Henry T., 109 [13]

Kutner, Bernard, 53 [79]

laboratory tests, 36–37, 97

Ladimer, Irving, 159 [39] [40], 160 [45] [46]

Lane, Marc J., 134 [10]

Larson, William R., 96 [9]

lawyers, *see* malpractice lawyers

Lawyers Interested in Victim's Equity (LIVE), 123 [4]

Lee, Philip R., 44 [34] [35] [36], 45 [39] [42] [43], 46 [44] [45] [47]

LeMaitre, George D., 68, 73 [13]

Lentz, Edith M., 24 [28], 59–60 [11], 63 [26], 199

Lepley, Derward, Jr., 22 [22]

Lesher, Stephan, 237

Lesser, Doris, 62 [21]

Levin, Lowell S., 178 [23] [24], 179 [25] [26], 188 [59]

Lewis, Leon, 19 [11] [16], 20 [17]

Lipson, Albert J., 136 [16], 138 [26], 141–42 [38]

Louisell, David W., 45 [41]

Lowrey, George H., 201

McDermott, Walsh, 41 [24], 53 [77] [78]
McDonald, Herbert B., 40 [21], 42 [29], 43 [30] [31]
McGarrah, Robert E., Jr., 171 [4], 172 [9]
McGill, William J., 34
McLamb, J. T., 48 [51]
Magraw, Richard H., 59 [8], 63–64 [28], 68, 73 [10] [14], 87 [24], 132 [4]
malpractice, 3, 5, 7
malpractice claims (including suits), 5, 6–7, 17, 27, 30, 51, 76, 103–4, 108–9, 110–13, 150, 155, 156–67, 160, 197, 207, 226
malpractice crisis, 103–20, 166–67; debate on, 121–30; defensive medicine as reaction to, 131–42; legislation as reaction to, 143–61
malpractice insurance, 103–20, 123–24, 146–49, 164–68
malpractice lawyers, 121–22, 123, 125–30, 150
malpractice legislation, 143–61
Marieskind, Helen I., 179 [27] [29], 182 [42]
Mauksch, Hans O., 20 [17], 26 [32], 32 [57], 65 [35]
Meador, Clifton K., 37 [5]
Mechanic, David, 63 [25], 195
Medicaid, 74–75
medical activism, 38, 52–53, 71, 85, 133–34
medical consumerism, 169–77, 188–89
medical diagnosis, 42–44, 135–36
medical discipline, 162–64
Medical Economics, 3, 76, 115, 131, 136, 137, 138, 139, 140, 172, 195
medical faddism, 40–41, 48–49, 52–53, 71, 184
medical injury, *see* injury, medical
medical model, *see* biomedical model
medical professional liability insurance, *see* malpractice insurance
medical research, 38–39, 58–59, 84, 88
medical risk, *see* risk, medical
medical schools, 39, 82, 87–88, 99
medical self-care, 169, 177–79, 182, 184–89
medical self-help, 169, 180–89
Medical Society of Virginia, 136, 138
medical technology, *see* technology, medical
medical training, 58–59; *see also* hospitals—teaching hospitals
Medicare, 74–75
medication error, 27–29, 201
medications, *see* drugs

Mellinkoff, Sherman M., 44 [33]
Menzies, Isabel E. P., 24 [26]
Merritt, Richard, 144 [5], 145 [8], 146 [12], 149 [16], 151 [23], 162 [48]
Meyer, Bernard C., 54 [83], 56 [91]
Millman, Marcia, 53 [78]
Minnesota Hospital Association, 165
Morris, Crawford, 30 [45]
Morris, P. J., 52 [73]
Moser, Robert H., 41 [27], 87 [23]
Mueller, Marjorie Smith, 18 [8], 39 [15], 186 [54]
Muller, Charlotte, 50 [61]
Murphy, Marvin L., 53 [78]
Myerhoff, Barbara, 96 [9]

Nader, Ralph, 170
National Association of Insurance Commissioners, 27 [35], 51 [67], 115, 150, 155, 157, 160 [43] [47], 197, 207, 226
National Institutes of Health, 38–39, 59
Negrete, Vida Francis, 196
Neuhauser, Duncan, 53 [78]
Newman, George F., 7 [6]
Newman, Stanley, 45 [41]
New York County Medical Society, 122
New York State Assembly Standing Committee on Health and Standing Committee on Insurance, 163 [51]
New York State Consumer Protection Board, 163
New York State Special Advisory Panel on Medical Malpractice (McGill Commission), Report of the, 105 [2], 113 [24], 148 [13], 156 [33], 158 [36] [37] [38]
New York State Trial Lawyers Association, 125 [8], 127 [18]
no-fault compensation system, 161
North American Reinsurance Corporation, 109
North Carolina Memorial Hospital, 48
Northrup, George, 132 [2]
nosocomial infection, 29–31, 201
nurses, 23–26, 28–29, 59–61, 62; relation to doctors, 25–26

Olsen, Donna M., 195
operations, *see* surgery
Orenland, Jerome D., 54–55 [86]
Orwell, George, xii
Our Bodies, Ourselves, 182, 186–87

Parsons, Talcott, 12 [24], 18 [9], 38 [11], 40 [19], 52 [76], 196

Pasanen, Wayne E., 31 [52]
Pasteur, Louis, 80, 81, 82
penicillin, *see* antibiotics
Pennsylvania Hospital Association, 166
Pertschuk, Michael, 174 [15]
Peterson, James L., 6 [3]
Physicians Crisis Committee, 123, 124, 128–29 [23], 130 [24]
Pidoux, 81
Pocincki, Leon S., 52 [75]
Porter, Jane, 45 [41], 47 [49]
Powles, John, 80 [3], 81 [8], 82–83 [11]
Prahalad, Coimbatore K., 40 [20]
prepaid group practice, 71–72
pretrial screening panels, 157–58
public health, 81

Rand Corporation, 138
Rasmussen, Howard, 85 [17], 215
res ipsa loquitur, 153–54
Riessman, Frank, 180 [33], 181 [34] [36] [37], 183 [46]
risk, medical, 10–11, 27, 29, 31–32, 34–36, 41–42, 43, 45–58, 51–52, 64–65, 139–40
risk management, 166
Roddis, Richard S. L., 105 [3], 110 [16], 117 [43]
Rogge, Paula, 224
Rosen, George, 81 [6]
Rubsamen, David S., 139 [30]
Ruzek, Sheryl K., 179 [27], 180 [30] [31]

St. Paul Fire & Marine Insurance Company, 113, 167
San Francisco Trial Lawyers, 125 [10], 127 [17]
Sawyer, Robert B., 135 [13]
Schimmel, Elihu M., 42 [28], 44 [32], 48 [50]
scientific medicine, *see* biomedical model; technology, medical
Secretary's Commission on Medical Malpractice, Report of the, 107 [10], 111 [18] [19], 112 [20], 114 [26] [27] [28], 114–15 [29], 115 [32], 118 [50], 132 [2], 219
self-care, medical, *see* medical self-care
self-help, medical, *see* medical self-help
Senger, Lester E., 109–10 [14]
Shapiro, Arthur K., 13 [27]
Sheldon, Alan, 36–37 [4], 78
Shenkin, Budd N., 173, 175–76

Shiloh, Ailon, 32 [59]
Shopper's Guide to Surgery, 171, 177
Sidel, Ruth, 181 [35], 183 [47]
Sidel, Victor W., 181 [35], 183 [47]
Silver, George A., 59 [6]
Silverman, Milton, 44 [34] [35] [36], 45 [39] [42] [43], 46 [44] [45] [47]
Simmons, Henry E., 45 [38] [40], 49 [55]
Simmons, Leo H., 19 [11] [16], 20 [17], 32 [56]
Singer, Peter, 100 [14]
Singleton, Henry E., 119
Skillman, John Joakim, 52 [72]
Skipper, James K., Jr., 21 [19], 26 [32] [33], 27 [34], 31 [53], 32 [57]
Smith, Adam, 94 [2]
Smith, Ester Gottlieb, 224
smokEnders, 181, 186
Solomon, Joel, 159 [39] [40], 160 [45] [46]
Somers, Anne R., 70–71 [6]
Somers, Herman M., 70–71 [6], 166 [66]
Sommer, Robert, 20 [17], 21 [20]
Soskis, Carol A., 172 [10]
specialization, 62–66; of doctors, 57–59, 63–67, 84, 98, 133, 137–38; of nurses, 60; of allied health personnel, 61, 62, 63, 66; of hospital employees, 62, 86, 98
Spiro, Howard M., 132 [5], 133 [8], 133–34 [9]
statistics: allied health personnel, 61–62; clinical lab personnel, 211; defensive medicine, 135–39; doctors, 58; doctors' incomes, 69–70; drugs, 44–45; health-care expenditures, 186; health workers, 58; hospital employees, 62; hospital insurance, 18; hospitals, 17, 40, 75, 197; iatrogenesis, 43, 47–48, 51–52; interns and residents, 58; lab tests, 36; malpractice arbitration, 160; malpractice claims, 17, 30, 51, 76, 108–9, 111–13, 150, 155, 157, 197, 207, 226; malpractice insurance, 106, 114, 116; medical-research expenditures, 39; nurses, 60–61; patient attitudes, 76, 195; prescriptions, 44; specialists, 58, 59; surgeons, 51, 58, 207; surgery, 51–52, 207; teaching hospitals, 39
statute of limitations, 156–57
Sterling, Peter, 204
Stevens, Rosemary, 10 [20], 19 [14], 39 [14], 58 [2] [3]
Steves, Buddy, 6 [5], 71 [7], 111 [19], 113 [22], 194

Stewart, Richard E., 105 [3], 110 [16], 117 [43]
Stolley, Paul D., 45 [38] [40], 49 [55]
Strodel, Robert C., 123 [3], 126 [15]
Suffolk County Medical Society, 160, 231
surgeons, 51, 53–56, 58, 70, 71, 72, 77, 136, 138, 207
surgery, 50–56, 71, 72, 76–77, 97, 207, 208, 209
Szasz, Thomas S., 54 [85], 237

Tagliacozzo, Daisy L., 20 [17], 26 [32], 31 [54], 32 [57], 65 [35]
Taylor, Carol, 13 [25], 22 [23], 65 [36], 202
Taylor, Gordon, 51 [70]
technology, medical, 11, 18, 19, 35–56, 75, 85–86, 94–95, 97, 133, 135–36
Teledyne, Inc., 118–20
Terkel, Studs, 98
thalidomide, 46–47
Thomas, Lewis, 88 [28] [29]
Titmuss, Richard M., 99 [13], 218
Todd, Malcolm C., 121
tonsillectomies, 41, 51, 53

University of Florida Teaching Hospital, 48

van Leeuwenhoek, Anton, 80
Virchow, Rudolf, 81

Waldron, Ingrid, 44 [37], 50 [59]
Wallace, James F., 45 [41]
Wanner, Rudolf G., 30 [47]
Warner, David C., 173, 175–76
Warner, Kenneth E., 40 [19]
Warren, David G., 144 [5], 145 [8], 146 [12], 149 [16], 151 [23], 162 [48]
Weight Watchers, 181, 186
Weinberger, Caspar, 226
Weinstein, Bernard M., 62 [21]
Werchick, Jack, 126 [14]
Wessen, Albert F., 20 [17], 25 [29]
Whitehorn, John C., 237
Wilcox, Robert B., 111 [17]
Wildavsky, Aaron, 193
Williams, Harold, 45 [41]
Wilson, Robert N., 24 [28], 59–60 [11], 62 [22] [23], 63 [24] [26], 67 [41], 199
Wolfe, Sidney M., 170
Wolff, Harold G., 19 [11] [16], 20 [17], 32 [56]
women's health movement, 179–80, 182, 187–88
Wriston, Henry M., 185

Yale University Medical School, 88
Yale University Medical Service, 48

Zurek, Robert C., 46 [45] [46], 52 [74]